MAGIC HOURS

BY
ARTHUR I. GATES
AND
JEAN Y. AYER

ILLUSTRATED BY
A. GLADYS PECK

NEW YORK
THE MACMILLAN COMPANY
1945

Set up and electrotyped. Published January, 1932. Reprinted March, 1932; August, 1932; April, 1933; July, 1933; September, 1933; December, 1933; April, 1934; January, 1935; May, 1935; July, 1935; January, 1936; September, 1936; January, 1937; May, 1937; June, 1938; November, 1939; April, 1944; December, 1944 February, 1945

— PRINTED IN THE UNITED STATES OF AMERICA —

ACKNOWLEDGMENTS

For permission to use copyrighted material, grateful acknowledgment is made to the following authors and publishers:

The Century Company for "Going Too Far," by Mildred Howells, from *St. Nicholas Magazine;* and for "The Tidy Lion," from *A Book of Cheerful Cats* (Copyright, 1892), by J. G. Francis.

Doubleday, Doran and Company, Inc. for "The Princess Who Could Not Cry" ("The Princess Who Laughed Too Much"), from *The Rainbow Cat* (Copyright, 1923), by Rose Fyleman; and to Methuen and Company, Ltd. (London) for the same selection.

E. P. Dutton and Company, Inc. for "The Timid Truck," from *A Merry-Go-Round of Modern Tales,* by Caroline D. Emerson; and for "Christmas Snow" and "In the Train," from *Childhood,* by Katherine Pyle.

Harcourt, Brace and Company for "Chairoplane Chant" and "The Sampler," from *Magpie Lane,* by Nancy Byrd Turner.

Dr. Smith Ely Jelliffe for "Clovers," by Helena Leeming Jelliffe.

Longmans, Green and Company for "Sinterklaas and Pieterbaas" and "Three Meals Shorten the Day," from *Wonder Tales from Windmill Lands,* by Frances Jenkins Olcott.

Lothrop, Lee and Shepard Company for "A Molasses-Cake Story," from *Inger Johanne's Lively Doings,* by Dikken Zwilgmeyer (Translator, Emilie Poulsson).

The Macmillan Company for "The Cat and Susannah" from *The Cat and the Captain,* by Elizabeth Coatsworth; "Bingo and the Angry Rooster" and "Charlie Rides with the Engineer," from *Charlie and His Puppy Bingo,* by Helen Hill and Violet Maxwell; "Little Tonino" from *Little Tonino,* by Helen Hill and Violet Maxwell; "A Soap Story" from *Soap Bubbles,* by Ellen Beers McGowan; "Playing Airplane," from *Playing Airplane,* by John F. McNamara; "The Golden Goose," from *Goldtree and Silvertree*, by Katharine Duncan Morse; "A Letter from a Pioneer," from *Letters of Polly the Pioneer*, by Stella Humphrey Nida; "Whistling Wejack," from *Holiday Meadow*, by Edith M. Patch; and "The Water Buffalo's Bath," from *Traveling Shops*, by Dorothy Rowe.

Macrae Smith Company for "What Puzzled the Robins" ("The Puzzled Robins"), from *The Way of the Wild*, by Clarence Hawkes.

Miss Blanche Jennings Thompson for "Magic."

The Viking Press for "The Rabbit," from *Under the Tree* (Copyright, 1922, B. W. Huebsch, Inc.), by Elizabeth Madox Roberts.

For many of the details given in "An Ink-Bottle Story," the author is indebted to *The Story Your Ink Bottle Tells*, a pamphlet published by the Carter Ink Company, Boston, Massachusetts.

For assistance in connection with compiling the content of *Magic Hours*, the editors wish to make special acknowledgment, for gracious and sympathetic coöperation, to Mrs. Rosalind Scharf and Miss Marian Leonard, New York Public Library (Jackson Square Branch); and, for valuable suggestions, to Miss Elizabeth Knapp, late Children's Librarian, Detroit, Michigan.

For critical reading of the manuscript grateful acknowledgment is due to Miss Laura Mengert and Miss Mary Mulholland, Educational Department, The Macmillan Company; and to Miss Roma Gans, Associate in Education, Teachers College; Miss Bess M. Young, Specialist in Upper Elementary Grades, Lincoln School, Teachers College; Mrs. Celeste Comegys Peardon, Co-author of the *Gates-Peardon Practice Exercises in Reading;* and to Dr. Georgina S. Gates, Barnard College, Columbia University.

For especially valuable assistance in testing the reading material and exercises, thanks are due to Mr. Robert J. Newbury, Principal, William Carter and Avery Schools, Needham Heights, Massachusetts; and to Miss Nina F. Palmer, Principal, and Mrs. Agnes A. Myers and Mrs. Celeste Bryant, Teachers, Mamaroneck Avenue School, White Plains, New York.

CONTENTS

I. Friends in Feathers and Fur

PAGE

The Tidy Lion . . . *Joseph G. Francis* 2
The Puzzled Robins . . . *Clarence Hawkes* 3
1. The Nests 3
2. The Mystery Is Explained . . . 12

Bingo and the Angry Rooster
Helen Hill and Violet Maxwell 19

Whistling Wejack . . . *Edith M. Patch* 31
1. "Freezing" 31
2. Polly Woodchuck 39
3. The Wejack Family 43

The Cat and Susannah . *Elizabeth Coatsworth* 51
The Rabbit . . . *Elizabeth Madox Roberts* 63

II. Schools of Long Ago

Books Never Tell . . . *Annette Wynne* 66
Schools of Long Ago . . . *Jean Y. Ayer* 68
The Sampler . . . *Nancy Byrd Turner* 78
Great-Grandfather's School Days *Jean Y. Ayer* 80
A Letter from a Pioneer . *Stella Humphrey Nida* 94

III. For Fun

PAGE

Going Too Far . . . . . *Mildred Howells* 106

Dr. Dolittle and the Pirates . *Hugh Lofting* 108

1. Red Sails and Blue Wings 109
2. The Rats' Warning 114
3. The Barbary Dragon 121
4. The Friendly Sharks 126

The Princess Who Laughed Too Much *Rose Fyleman* 133

1. The Princess 133
2. Marigold 138
3. A Surprise 142

IV. Everyday Things

Magic . . . *Blanche Jennings Thompson* 150

An Ink-Bottle Story . . . *Jean Y. Ayer* 151

A Soap Story . . . . *Ellen Beers McGowan* 163

1. Jimmy's Questions 163
2. Setting Back the Clock 173

V. Folk Tales

Christmas Snow . . . . . *Katharine Pyle* 187

Sinterklaas and Pieterbaas *Frances Jenkins Olcott* 188

1. Out of Spain into Holland 188
2. Out of Holland into America 193

Three Meals Shorten the Day *Frances Jenkins Olcott* 197

PAGE

The Golden Touch . . . *Nathaniel Hawthorne* 207
1. Midas and His Treasure 207
2. The Wish 210
3. The Golden Touch 213
4. Another Wish 221

VI. Make-Believe

The Old Brass Pot . . . *Hilda Conkling* 231
The Golden Goose . *Katharine Duncan Morse* 233
Scene 1. 234
Scene 2. 247
Clovers . . . . *Helena Leeming Jelliffe* 260

VII. Children in Other Lands

A Molasses-Cake Story . *Dikken Zwilgmeyer* 263
1. Molasses Cakes and a Joke 263
2. The Lost Is Found 270
The Water Buffalo's Bath . *Dorothy Rowe* 281
Little Tonino . *Helen Hill and Violet Maxwell* 294
1. Tonino's Home 294
2. The Town Wall and the Castle 303
3. The Morning 306
4. The Afternoon 312

VIII. Wheels and Wings

In the Train . . . . . *Katharine Pyle* 323
Charlie Rides with the Engineer
Helen Hill and Violet Maxwell 324
1. The Train 324
2. The Engine 330

PAGE

Seeing Lindbergh Off . . . *Jean Y. Ayer* 341

Playing Airplane . . *John F. McNamara* 354

1. How to Make the Airplane . . . 354
2. How to Operate Your Plane 359
3. What Happens as We Fly 364
4. Doing Stunts 369
5. Coming Down 376

Chairoplane Chant . . *Nancy Byrd Turner* 382

The Timid Truck . . *Caroline D. Emerson* 384

A Short Dictionary 396

1. Helps in Pronouncing 396
2. Dictionary Word List 397

I

FRIENDS IN FEATHERS AND FUR

THE TIDY LION

A lion emerged from his lair
For a short summer cut for his hair;
  But the poor barber wept,
  While the customers slept,
As they waited a turn in the chair.

—J. G. Francis.

THE PUZZLED ROBINS

1. The Nests

One spring when Cock Robin and My Lady came north, they decided that they would seek a new nesting place. They had been having rather poor luck with their babies for several years; so they felt that they must try to find a new place for a home.

For three years they had built in an apple tree in a farmer's dooryard. This had been a fine place for their nest. They had enjoyed the farmer and his wife, and the children were very friendly, but there were some drawbacks.

The farmer kept a number of cats. Each time the new little robins were crowded out of the nest one, at least, was sure to be eaten.

The starlings also troubled them. The grackles were likewise not on good terms with the robin family. But, worst of all, a crow had found the nest one morning very early, before the farmer was up, and had robbed it of every small bird. If the farmer had been up, he would probably have spoken to Mr. Crow with his gun; but the crow was too early for the farmer.

For all these reasons, the robins decided that they must have a new home. They looked about for a long time. Finding a really fine place for a nest is a task that takes patience — so many things have to be considered. They investigated any number of orchards and barns before they finally made a decision. The place that they chose pleased them both very much, but what it was or what it was used for they did not know.

It was not far from a railroad depot at the end of a small country line. There was only one train a day and that went to the city in the morning and returned at night.

There were a great many iron beams and cross-beams in the new location, and the place they chose for a nest was rather dark and hidden. Cock Robin felt sure that cats never came there. They discovered this spot about nine o'clock one morning. The train had gone to the city two hours before, and the yard was quiet. In fact it was nearly always quiet there, except at morning and evening.

The robins had wasted so much time searching that they went to work at once, and by night they had the nest partly built. Mud and dry grass had been plenty and they had never before made such progress. They roosted in a tree near-by that night, feeling very happy over the day's work.

The next morning they did not go to see the nest until the train had left and the

yard had become quiet. You can well imagine their astonishment to find the nest gone. The beam on which they had placed it was there, but no nest was to be seen. Neither were there any signs of their work. When a nest is blown down, there is usually some mud left clinging to the place, but the beam was quite clean.

The robins were much puzzled, but they set to work again with a will. The birds and other wild creatures have a patience that puts to shame the best efforts of man. If they do not succeed at first, they try again. So the busy pair worked very hard all day, and by night they had a new nest half done.

Cock Robin was the first to look at the nest on the following morning and he hastened to report to My Lady. The new nest that they had worked on the day before was gone, but the old one was back. He could tell it because it was shaped a little differently than the other and they had used more straw in it. My Lady laughed at him, but he stuck to it that it was the nest they had worked on two days before.

" Well," said My Lady, " I am just as well suited with this one. Let's finish it." So they went to work, and by night the nest was nearly completed. It needed only a few finishing touches and some shaping which My Lady always did herself. The robins went to roost that night feeling very well pleased. Cock Robin prolonged his evening song because he was so happy about the nearly finished home.

When he flew to the nest in the morning, his beak was full of straw. He dropped the straw at the first sight of the nest and hurried away to tell his wife.

The nest that had been so nearly completed was gone, and the half-built nest was back in its place. The robins were both greatly troubled, and flew back and forth with much complaining. Some one was playing them a mean trick — there was no doubt about that. But My Lady finally persuaded her husband that this nest was almost as good as the other and that if they hurried they might finish it that day. So they worked with a will, and by night it was done.

In spite of their trials, it was a very happy pair of robins that went to roost that night. On the morrow, there would be a robin's blue egg in the nest.

My Lady was the first to inspect the nest

in the morning. In fact she went to lay the first egg of the set. But she soon came flying to Cock Robin with strange news. The completed nest was gone and in its place was the nearly completed one.

Cock Robin could not explain the mystery. He could only chirp in a puzzled way and fly about.

Finally he and My Lady together finished the nest in the forenoon, and in the afternoon My Lady laid the first egg. It was very large for a robin's egg, and of a beautiful blue, and she was justly proud of it.

As soon as the train had gone on the following morning she flew to the nest. She would lay another egg that day. She was feeling very cheerful.

You can perhaps imagine her astonishment to find that the nest with the egg in it was not there. The other nest, which they had finished two days before, was back and there was of course no egg in it.

Although My Lady was astonished beyond bird expression, yet she set to work to repair the damage by laying a second egg. But this egg was not so large, and was not quite so deep a blue as the first one.

Cock Robin himself went to inspect the nest on the following morning. To tell the truth, these sudden disappearances of the nests were getting on his nerves. He came back with a strange report. The nest with the large blue egg was back, but the other nest was gone.

"Well," said My Lady, "I don't like it; but as long as we have a nest with one egg in it, let's be satisfied."

"But," said Cock Robin, "we have two nests and each one has an egg in it."

But My Lady was so interested in laying her eggs that she did not trouble her head about it. She laid another egg in the nest with the large one.

Wonder of wonders! On the morrow, the

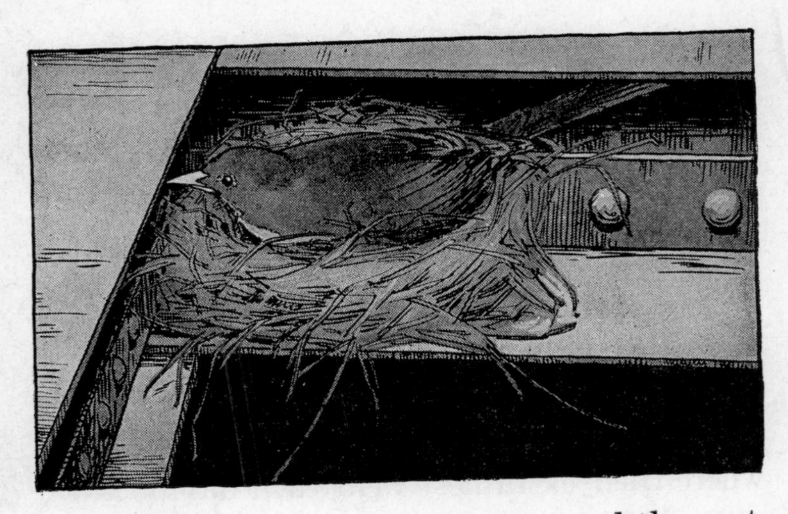

nest with two eggs in it was gone and the nest with the small egg in it was back. This really alarmed Cock Robin. But My Lady made the best of it and laid another egg beside the small one.

That night after My Lady was asleep on the roost — for she had been so disturbed that she had not dared to stay on the nest — brave Cock Robin decided that he would guard the nest and find out what it was that stole their home away each day. So he sat upon the eggs all night.

2. The Mystery Is Explained

In the morning the train came in, was made up as usual, and went away to the city. But it had barely left the station when a greatly excited Cock Robin flew away to find My Lady and tell her the wonderful story. It had been a terrible ordeal for the brave little bird, but he had solved the mystery. He knew where their extra nest went each day.

Cock Robin had been very comfortable on the nest all night. He had begun to think that it was not going to leave them that day when the trainmen started to make up the train in the yard.

Presently the Great Thunderer, as the robins called the engine, was detached from the train and came roaring and hissing along the shiny rails toward the place where poor little Cock Robin was sitting on his nest. He was terribly frightened and was about to fly away when it passed above him. Either he could not fly out then, or he was too much scared to fly.

He heard the talk of the men above, and then the beams, the crossbeams, and Cock Robin and his nest began slowly moving. They swung around further and further and finally stood still. Then the Great Thunderer rolled away snorting and thundering. The robins had made their nests on a beam of a turntable that turned early every morning to bring the engine around.

Cock Robin, frightened nearly to death, flew out from under the turntable and went to tell his wife.

The trainmen saw him go and later discovered the nest. They also found the second nest at the other end of the turntable.

"Plucky little fellows, aren't they?" said one man. "Let's watch them and see how they make it go. It must seem strange to them to have their two houses shifted about each day."

In a very few minutes both robins came back and Cock Robin proudly showed his wife the second nest only twenty feet away and quite as secure as its fellow.

But My Lady was very much disturbed, and not much pleased over her mate's discovery.

"I can't sit on the eggs in both nests at once. What can I do? Half the eggs will spoil."

"Well, we will see," said her mate, who was so pleased with himself for solving the mystery that he did not worry about the second nest. But he grew quite excited when his mate announced a plan. In fact, he was very angry at her suggestion.

"You must sit on the eggs in the second nest. That is the only way," announced My Lady. "I am not going to lay eggs for nothing."

Cock Robin protested that he would spoil his plumage, that he would have no time to

get food, and made many other excuses, but his wife had her way. Poor Cock Robin sat on the extra eggs, and he and My Lady hatched two broods of young robins.

The trainmen watched them all through the process. They were so impressed with the robins' courage that they left food for them, and that was a great help.

Finally when it was time for the two broods to be crowded out of the nests, the trainmen picked the little birds up under the turntable and placed them in trees near-by. They were safer here than on the ground, and the four young birds all lived.

But when Cock Robin proposed that they raise another brood, on one nest this time, My Lady struck. She said that two broods were enough for that year and that she wasn't going to live under the Great Thunderer any longer. So they took their four children to a near-by orchard and spent a very pleasant summer.

This is a strange romance in birdland, but the trainmen who told me the story say that it is true, and I give it to you just as I received it from them.

— Clarence Hawkes (*Adapted*).

Do You Know?

Copy the numbers of the 12 questions. After each number on your paper, write the answer in one word. You will find the 12 answers among the 16 words below the questions.

1. Where do robins fly for the winter season?
2. What four-legged enemies did Cock Robin and My Lady find at the farmhouse?
3. What birds sometimes steal young robins?
4. What other birds were not on good terms with the robin family?
5. What holds a robin's nest together?
6. What else do robins use in building?
7. What color are a robin's eggs?
8. How many eggs did the mother robin lay before she sat on them to hatch them out?
9. Where did the robins build their nest?
10. Who helped the robin family?
11. Where did the robins spend the summer?
12. What is a mystery?

crows	puzzle	brown	turntable
grass	cats	question	orchard
south	mud	grackles	five
trainmen	four	blue	dogs

Things to Do

1. The story "What Puzzled the Robins" is from an interesting book named *The Way of the Wild* by Clarence Hawkes. Another book — all about birds — that you would enjoy is *Bird Stories* by Edith M. Patch.

2. Make a list of ten birds and tell or write one thing you know about each.

3. In a dictionary, all words are arranged in alphabetic order. To see how this is done, look at "A Short Dictionary" on pages 396–408. To use a dictionary quickly, you must know the order of the alphabet. Write the alphabet in two columns upon a sheet of paper. Then, after each letter except *x* and *z*, write a word that begins with that letter. Take your words from these three columns:

mystery	explain	wonder
justly	drawbacks	patience
nest	ordeal	completed
location	beam	inspect
however	astonished	used
grackle	quiet	roost
finally	very	turntable
kind	starling	your

BINGO AND THE ANGRY ROOSTER

One day Charlie and his mother and father and aunt and Topsy and Bingo and Jane all went to the country together. Charlie enjoyed the trip for he liked to ride on trains. But Topsy, the kitten, and Jane, the cat, had to travel all the way in baskets, which they did not like at all. Puppy Bingo had to travel all by himself in the baggage car, and he did not like that either.

But when at last they came to the farm where they were going to stay for a month, Charlie opened the baskets and let Jane and Topsy out. Then he unfastened Bingo's leash, and they all went exploring together. At first Jane and Topsy were afraid, but Bingo was delighted. Soon they all liked the country very much, and the longer they stayed the more they liked it.

There were many delightful things for cats and dogs to do, that they could not do in the city. Instead of long straight roads with automobiles dashing past all the time, there were fields and meadows to run around in. There were trees for Topsy to climb and nice muddy puddles for Bingo to roll in, and Jane could go out for long walks by herself without meeting anything dangerous.

Charlie got up very early in the country because he liked to see the cows milked. Topsy and Bingo and Jane liked to see the cows milked, too; so they went to the barn with him. Charlie always carried three little bowls to the barn; and Mr. Browne, the farmer, filled them with warm milk straight from the cow, so that Topsy and Bingo and Jane could have their breakfast without waiting to return to the house.

The milking interested them all, because at home their milk always came out of milk bottles that had been left at the door by a milkman. There were no cows in the city.

While Charlie was in the country he had a fine time exploring the fields and meadows, and of course Bingo followed him wherever he went. They waded in brooks and went fishing and saw wild rabbits and a woodchuck. It would take a whole book to tell you all the delightful things they did together.

Now, wouldn't you think that Bingo, with so much space to play in, and so many interesting things to do all day long, would have been able to keep out of mischief at least as long as he was in the country? But no, he could not. You see, puppies nearly always are in mischief. It is not that they want to make trouble, but that they like to play. So Bingo often went off by himself and thought of nice, mischievous things to do.

One of the things that Bingo liked to do more than anything else was to go and bark at the chickens. This frightened the chickens, and Charlie always stopped him when he found him doing it. But often Bingo would slip away from Charlie and dash down to the chicken house and bark, "Yap, yap, yap!"

He loved to see the hens running this way and that, clucking loudly and calling to the little chickens, who would come running to hide themselves under their mothers' wings.

Bingo enjoyed this tremendously and never tired of the game. Of course he never hurt any of the chickens or the hens. Bingo was really a good little puppy and he would not have done a thing like that, but he *did* like to watch them running around and he liked

to hear the hens saying, "Cluck, cluck, cluck, CLUCK!" This amused him very much.

One day Charlie was busy helping Mrs. Browne make butter. Bingo watched Charlie for a while as he thumped away with the dasher of the churn, but he soon got tired of watching and not doing anything himself. So he decided that he would go and play with the chickens.

He began to bark before he got to the chicken house, and the hens began to cluck, cluck, cluck, and the chickens ran this way and that way and scrambled under their mothers' wings.

Bingo was so busy with his barking that he did not notice that there was a newcomer among the hens. This was a big white rooster that Mr. Browne had brought home from a fair the night before.

He was a huge rooster. He had won a prize at the fair because he was so big. When Bingo jumped in among the hens, they were all so scared that they ran around and said, "Cluck, cluck, cluck, CLUCK," just as he expected they would. But the rooster was not scared — no, indeed. He opened his beak, and Bingo heard a tremendous sound — "Ooka-ooka-ooka-ooooooooo! Ooka-ooka-ooka-ooooooooo! Ooka-ooka-ooka-oooooo-ooo!" Then the rooster sprang up in the air, flapped his wings, and rushed at Bingo!

The little dog was so startled that he jumped backwards toward the chicken house, and the rooster dashed after him. All the hens came hurrying up and the chickens, too, saying, "Cluck, cluck, cluck, CLUCK." They seemed to be on every side! Poor Bingo was terribly frightened, as well he might be, for the rooster was really very much annoyed, and he would have pecked Bingo if he had caught him.

But he did not catch him. Just in the nick of time, Bingo saw the chicken house, and he managed to scramble in through the open door before the rooster caught him. He was safe!

Yes, he was safe, but he had to stay there! The rooster did not quite like to go in after Bingo (you see Bingo was really very nearly as big as the rooster); so he decided to keep Bingo a prisoner. He strutted solemnly up and down in front of the chicken-house door, and every time Bingo would try to come out he would crow, " Ooka-ooka-ooka-oooooooo! Ooka-ooka-ooka-ooooooooo! Ooka-ooka-ooka-oooooooo!" and scare Bingo so that he decided to stay where he was.

Poor Bingo! it seemed to him that he stayed hours and hours in the chicken house. He wondered if he would ever get out again. He was sure that it was long past his dinner hour, for he felt dreadfully hungry. Bingo was a very unhappy little dog.

At last Charlie had finished helping Mrs. Browne make the butter. They had taken it out of the churn, and Mrs. Browne had put it in a big wooden bowl and beaten it with wooden butter paddles and put cold water on it so that all the buttermilk was squeezed and washed out. She had given Charlie some butter in a smaller bowl so that he could finish making it by himself. Mrs. Browne had promised him that they should have it on the dinner table and surprise his mother and father.

But it wasn't dinner time yet, so Charlie ran into the garden to look for Bingo — and there was no Bingo to be seen! He called Bingo, but Bingo did not come. Then he decided to go down to the big barn to look for him.

As he passed near the chicken house he heard a great commotion — "Cluck, cluck, cluck, cluck, CLUCK," "Ooka-ooka-ooka-ooooooooo! Ooka-ooka-ooka-ooooooooo! Ooka-ooka-ooka-ooooooooo!" . . . Bingo had been trying to get out!

Then Charlie said, "Shoo, shoo, shoo!" and the hens and even the rooster all got out of the way, and Bingo was free again! Oh, how glad he was! He jumped, and pranced, and followed Charlie to the kitchen, where his dinner was waiting for him.

But never again did Bingo bark at the chickens and chase them. He no longer thought it an amusing game. In fact Bingo never went near the chicken house again.

Sometimes, for a joke, Charlie would say, "Do you want to go and see the chickens, Bingo?" At once, Bingo would droop his tail and wiggle as if he felt uncomfortable at the very thought — and he probably did.

— HELEN HILL AND VIOLET MAXWELL (*Adapted*).

SENTENCES TO FINISH

Write on a paper the numbers from 1 to 15. Then write after each number the words that have been left out in these sentences:

1. Charlie and his mother, father, and aunt all went —— —— ——.
2. Bingo had to travel by himself in —— —— ——.
3. Charlie got up early because he liked to see —— —— ——.
4. When he went to the barn, he always carried —— —— ——.
5. In the city, milk bottles were left at the door by —— ——.
6. Bingo liked very much to bark —— —— ——.
7. One day Charlie was helping Mrs. Browne —— ——.

8. Mr. Browne had brought a big rooster home from —— ——.

9. When the rooster chased Bingo, he ran into —— —— ——.

10. Bingo wondered if he would ever —— —— ——.

11. Mrs. Browne took the butter out —— —— ——.

12. Charlie went to the barn to look —— ——.

13. He heard a great noise near —— —— ——.

14. When Charlie saw the hens and roosters, he said —— —— ——.

15. Never again did Bingo bark —— —— ——.

THINGS TO DO

1. Perhaps you would like to read the rest of the book about Charlie and Bingo. It is named *Charlie and His Puppy Bingo* and was written by Helen Hill and Violet Maxwell.

2. If you have a dog, tell or write what you do to keep him well and happy. If you have no dog, tell what you would do if you had one.

3. How many different kinds of dogs do you know? It would be interesting to collect pictures of the different kinds and to find out something about each kind.

WHISTLING WEJACK

1. "Freezing"

One of his names was Wejack. One was Woodchuck. One was Ground Hog. One was Marmot. He had other names, too; though four seem enough, especially as he, himself, did not know any of the names people gave him. When he talked, he did not speak in words. He spoke in whistles. That is why Anne and Dick called him "Whistling Wejack." He lived in Holiday Meadow.

Holiday Meadow is a long field that reaches

from the margin of Holiday Stream to the foot of Holiday Hill.

Whistling Wejack lived at the end of the meadow nearest the hill. His home was a long underground tunnel and it had two doorways. One of these opened into a patch of clover in the meadow. The other was hidden by rocks.

Dick and Anne and little dog Sandy knew where Wejack's meadow hole was; but the hole between the rocks was so placed that no person or dog could get to it.

Sandy's chief interest in Wejack was the fun of sniffing down the opening of the tunnel and trying excitedly to dig the woodchuck out. Wejack did not seem much worried by the dog. His tunnel was long and his private doorway among the rocks at the other end was well guarded. In fact, Wejack sometimes lay quietly on top of the rocks, sunning himself, while he watched Sandy pawing at the hole far away in the clover garden.

Dick and Anne, however, did not care to disturb Wejack's home. They wished to become acquainted with him. So, usually, when they went to call on the woodchuck, they put Sandy in the shed and shut the door.

One day the cousins saw Wejack on top of his favorite rock at the foot of the hill. When they came rather near he slipped out of sight so quickly that they were not sure which way he had gone.

Now that they knew where he liked to sun himself they often came to visit him. Wejack would see them coming and would lie motionless. Unless they came too near he did not go away to hide. He hid in plain sight — just by keeping still. At such times he seemed like a part of the brown and gray shadows on the rock, and sometimes Dick and Anne used to look right at him without seeing him at all.

When they told Uncle David how hard it was to see the woodchuck, he explained that many wild creatures have a way of hiding by keeping motionless. " That method of escaping notice is called ' freezing,' " he said, " because the animal stays as still as if it were frozen and could not move."

So Dick and Anne learned to " freeze " by watching how the woodchuck did the trick. They found that birds and squirrels and rabbits and porcupines and other little wild creatures came quite near them when they stayed " frozen " long enough. In that way they saw a great deal more of the animals than they could have if they had been walking and talking.

The easiest way for them to play their freezing game was to sit down on the ground with their backs against a rock or a big tree trunk. Then, as long as they kept their hands and feet and heads still and did not fidget or whisper, they were all right. At such times the woodchuck used to come and go among the rocks or run down to feed in the clover as if there were no one near him.

But as soon as they became tired of keeping quiet and wriggled a little, Wejack would look at them at once. Next he would stand still and whistle at them. Perhaps he was trying to scare them away, but they were never frightened by his music. His whistling was clear and rather sweet, and they liked it.

Wejack had another amusing habit. When he stood on his hind legs, he always dropped his front paws. Dick and Anne giggled the first time they saw him do this.

"He looks too funny for words!" said Dick.

"He is just like a person who is trying hard to be graceful with his hands," said Anne.

Of course Wejack was not really trying to be graceful. His little paws dropped naturally in a pretty way.

After the grass grew tall in the meadow, Dick and Anne used sometimes to hide where they could see Wejack's front doorway in the clover garden. Beside this was a large mound of dirt that Wejack had piled there when he was digging his tunnel.

Sometimes they crept through the grass so slowly and quietly that Wejack did not know they were there. At least sometimes he did not know until the crow told him.

Of course Corbie, the crow, did not say, "Look out, Wejack, two children are creeping through the grass toward your hole." All Corbie did was to call, "Caw! Caw! Caw!"

and the chances are that he was not thinking about Wejack at all.

As a matter of fact it was Corbie's job to watch the meadow and warn the other crows when people went abroad. So when he saw the cousins from Holiday Farm, he said "Caw!" three times and flew to a tall pine on the hill to see where they were going.

A crow's signal may be intended only for the other crows. But to almost all the wild creatures of meadow and hillside and woodland it is a warning. When a crow caws three times in a certain tone, he means what a person would mean if he yelled, "Danger! Look out!"

Wejack, of course, could not see very far through the tall meadow grass. At such times he depended a great deal on Corbie's signals. Whenever he heard the warning voice of the crow he would stand on his hind legs in sudden alarm, gazing and sniffing first this way and then that, as if sure that danger must be near.

It was while Dick and Anne were sitting, one day, close enough to the mound to see Wejack as he stood before his open doorway, that they saw, too, his wonderful vanishing trick. The children were keeping as quiet as they could, but it was rather hard for them to stay "frozen" long where they had nothing to lean against; and after a while they moved a little — enough so that Wejack glanced at them. They breathed only short breaths and were so quiet that the woodchuck did not seem frightened. He did not dash quickly into his hole headfirst as he would have done if he were being chased.

Indeed, he did not seem to be moving at all. He sank backward bit by bit so slowly that, even while they watched, Dick and Anne could hardly see a motion. Only where there had been a woodchuck, erect with drooping paws, there was at last only a hole in the ground.

The children crept, very carefully, to the mound. For a moment near the top of the black hole they saw Wejack's bright eyes gleaming at them. Then even the eyes were gone!

2. Polly Woodchuck

Later the children discovered another woodchuck. They named her Polly. They found that one of her holes was very near the vegetable garden — too near, as it turned out.

One spring morning Uncle David came into the house and said, "A ground hog has been visiting our vegetable garden and eating most of the early planting peas."

"That must be our Polly Woodchuck," began Anne calmly. "She likes vegetables — *especially* peas. I saw her this morning when I went out to see the sun come up. Polly was eating her breakfast of young pea vines." Then Anne's voice trembled a little. "I thought I'd tell you," she said, "that Polly can have my share and I'll go without green peas this summer."

Dick looked at his uncle's face. There was almost a frown on his forehead and almost a smile at the corners of his mouth. "We'll chase Polly over to the hill, Uncle David, where she will not harm the garden any more!" he said quickly.

Polly had three holes opening from her tunnel. One was quite near the end of the peas in the garden. Two were under stone piles in the hedgerow between the garden and the meadow. The children had been watching the woodchuck for several days and knew where she ran when Sandy chased her.

It took the cousins all the morning to move the stones away from Polly's holes in the hedgerow. They carried a lot of the small stones to the garden and rolled them into the opening that was near the peas. Then they plugged the end of one of the other holes. The third one they left open so that Polly could come out easily without digging a new hole.

Polly stayed in her tunnel nearly all day. The noises near her doorways had frightened her. But late in the afternoon, as all seemed quiet, she came out of her one free hole and stood up and looked out. She rested one paw against the trunk of a tree and let the other droop. She turned her head and listened with her short ears. After a while she gave a long churr-rr-rr-ing whistle.

Dick, who was sitting on a branch of a big apple-tree near the hedgerow, heard her. He thought it was a lonesome-sounding whistle. Then from far up the meadow he heard another woodchuck calling. Polly heard the sound, too, and trotted along the meadow toward the hill.

Dick climbed down the tree and packed little stones into the remaining doorway of Polly's dugout. "Of course she can dig other holes if she wants to," he thought, "but maybe she will not care to come back. She hasn't had a very pleasant day here."

That evening at supper time, Uncle David asked, " What's the latest news of Polly? "

" Oh," said Dick cheerfully, " Whistling Wejack met her in the meadow and I think he invited her over to the hill."

Dick's guess was right. Polly did not come back to the garden. Instead she helped Wejack improve his home. They dug several more branches to his tunnel so as to have more doorways when they wished to go in or out. They made three or four little dugout rooms or dens in widened places in the tunnel. In these they spread comfortable beds of dry stubble and leaves.

They found their bedding in the meadow and on the hill and carried it home in their mouths. Sometimes they rested in one room and sometimes in another. They kept them all fresh and clean.

3. The Wejack Family

It was on a pleasant day in early summer, while Anne was sitting at the foot of the hill not far from one of Wejack's holes, that she saw seven little animals come out to play among the rocks.

They had fluffy bodies and very short legs. Their ears were little and their mouths drooped at the corners. They looked like Polly and Wejack but they were prettier and very small. They were lively little woodchucks and tumbled and rolled about on the ground, biting and hugging and tussling in joyful frolic.

During their play they ran quite near to Anne. She kept very still. One of her hands was resting on the ground and in it was a half-eaten chocolate candy. Two of the young woodchucks stopped near her and sniffed. Next they crept to her hand and tasted the candy. Then, quick as a flash, one of them pulled it out of her hand and went off with it.

Anne chuckled. "You darlings!" she said softly.

Wejack, all this time, had been sunning himself on his favorite rock. When Anne spoke, he looked at her and whistled softly. He did not seem very much worried. After all these weeks of seeing Anne frequently, he was rather used to her. Besides, it did not seem to be his task to take care of his seven sons and daughters. Polly liked to do that.

Polly took care of them now. She stood up near a rock, resting her paws on top of it. When she saw Anne, she whistled a long shrill command. Her seven children understood what she said to them and ran pell-mell for their nearest hole.

After that Dick and Anne came nearly every pleasant day to see the young woodchucks. They brought crackers soaked in milk, cookies, and chocolate candy. After placing these dainties near Wejack's door they sat down not far away and "froze" while they waited for the little woodchucks to come out for their treat.

At first the youngsters did not seem at all timid. They had not learned to be afraid. But Polly attended to their education, and the more she whistled to them when Dick and Anne were near the more shy they became.

Mr. and Mrs. Wejack and the seven young Wejacks were very busy during the late summer and fall. They were getting food enough to last them all winter. They did not gather extra food and store it away as squirrels and muskrats and beavers and certain other of their relatives do. They prepared for winter

as bears and raccoons do — by eating as much as they could of the best tasting food they found and getting very, very fat indeed.

Early in the season the woodchucks had enjoyed eating dandelion blossoms, but of course they did not find many of these flowers in the fall. There were plenty of other kinds, however. The late blossoms of red clover tasted good to them and they liked these even after the flowers had gone to seed. Indeed, they ate the seeds of various plants, including some grain. Seeds are fattening; so the diet they chose was the best sort for them.

By the time really cold weather came, the nine woodchucks were all so fat that their plump bodies were rather heavy for such short legs to carry. They seemed lazy in their motions. There came an extra chilly day, when they were too lazy to make any motions at all. They just lay curled up in the warm beds in their dens with their noses tucked under their round stomachs and slept.

Exactly how long they stayed there I cannot tell you. There is an old story, as perhaps you know, that woodchucks always wake on the second day of February and come out to test the weather. If the sun is shining, as it does on a snappy clear cold day, so the story goes, the woodchucks see their shadows and return to their dens for another nap of six weeks. If they do not see their shadows, they stay awake.

Such old stories are interesting, though they cannot be taken for fact. This much, however, is certain — these animals have that one day in the year named for them. The second of February is known in our calendar as Ground-Hog Day.

— EDITH M. PATCH (*Adapted*).

WHICH IS RIGHT?

Write on a paper the numbers from 1 to 10. Read the questions and answers and write on your paper, after the number of each question, the correct answer for that question.

I

1. When Wejack talked, how did he speak?
   In whispers.
   In whistles.
   In whines.
2. What was Wejack's home?
   An old kennel.
   A large round tank.
   An underground tunnel.

3. Where was one of Wejack's doorways?

In a patch of clover.

In a piece of carpet.

In a pile of cedar.

4. How did Wejack sometimes hide?

By fleeing.

By fading.

By "freezing."

II

5. What did Anne see Polly doing?

Eating young pea vines.

Eating young grapevines.

Eating yellow carrots.

6. How did Dick and Anne keep Polly out of the garden?

They scared her with stones.

They stayed near her tunnel.

They stopped up her doorways.

7. What did Polly help Wejack to do?

Improve his home.

Find a new home.

Dig in the garden.

III

8. What did Anne see one day?
   - Seven little animals.
   - Six little airplanes.
   - Seven little anchors.

9. What did the woodchucks take from Anne?
   - A Christmas candle.
   - A cooked cabbage.
   - A chocolate candy.

10. What did the woodchucks do in winter?
    - They camped out and slept.
    - They curled up and slept.
    - They rested and ate.

Things to Do

1. The story of "Whistling Wejack" is taken from a book by Edith M. Patch named *Holiday Meadow*. Perhaps you will like to read the other stories in it. Another book by Miss Patch that is something like *Holiday Meadow* is *Holiday Pond*.

2. Play that you are Dick or Anne. Tell about Wejack's tunnel, or about how you got Polly to move, or about the seven little woodchucks. If you like, play instead that you are little dog Sandy and tell about Wejack's tunnel.

THE CAT AND SUSANNAH

The Cat was furious. Not a door or window of the house was open. He went to the front door and mewed. He went to the side door — which was almost never used — and mewed. Then he went to the back door and there he mewed loudest and longest.

He could hear Susannah, the Captain's housekeeper, walking around the kitchen, singing to herself. She was always humming to herself like a bumble-bee. When something happened to make her excited, she made up songs, mostly complaining ones, telling how she felt. The Cat knew that Susannah heard him there at her door with his feet in the damp and was glad to keep him out.

If only the Captain were home, he would call, "Susannah! Ship ahoy! Lower the gangway to take on passengers!" But the Captain had taken his cane and gone to see his married daughter. Goodness knows when he'd be back.

The Cat picked his way across the grass, shaking the wet off his feet, for it had been raining. Poor Cat, he hated it! He was thinking of the cushioned chair indoors by the fire where he loved to sit watching the flames with sleepy eyes and purring to himself. But he didn't feel like purring now. He climbed up the lilac bush. He knew just where to put each small paw, just how much spring to give, and how deep to stick his claws into the bark. He did everything beautifully. But the leaves shook raindrops down his neck and made him bristle his whiskers.

He climbed a low branch and looked in at the kitchen window. There was Susannah rolling dough for the biscuits the Captain liked. She was little and old and fat, and she wore on her head a big red bandanna. When she saw the Cat, she began to laugh and point her finger at him. He could hear her singing:

"Old Mister Cat, he climbed up a tree.
What do you want, Cat, starin' at me?
You won't get hurt by a little nice rain,
So when you get tired, you can climb
down again!"

The Cat saw it was no use. Susannah did not like him, and he knew very well she had several good reasons for it. He mewed one last mew, just in case she should change her mind. Then he gave her a hard look, and went down the lilac, headfirst.

He knew now he would have to wait until the Captain came back, but he wouldn't forget Susannah's meanness — not he! He picked his way through the grass, lifting his feet high and walking around the puddles, and went in under the veranda by the little opening that only he knew about. There he sat, out of anyone's sight, switching his big black tail.

About five o'clock the Captain came home. He was not a big man but he carried a very big umbrella. He had wrinkles around his eyes from looking long distances, and he walked as though the street were going up and down under him, because he had spent so much of his time on the decks of boats. Everybody loved the Captain the moment they saw him because he was so kind and so jolly.

The cat loved him, too, but he took a

naughty pride in not showing it, except sometimes when they were alone together. Then he would jump on the Captain's knee and rub his head against the Captain's chin, and go to sleep curled in the hollow of his arm. And how careful the Captain would be not to move!

They understood each other very well, and the Captain used to say that he had never shipped with a better shipmate than his black cat. But to-day the Cat was in a bad humor, as he walked out from under the veranda.

"Well, well, there you are, hey?" said the Captain, and he opened the door and held it and waited for the Cat to come in. But the Cat only looked at him. He was being provoking.

"Don't you want to come in?" asked the Captain.

The Cat still looked at him — almost in the doorway but not quite.

"All right," said the Captain, "if you won't, you won't, my lad," and he started to shut the door.

But before he could get it shut, the Cat came into the room.

It was a curious room, though neither the Cat nor the Captain thought so. It was both living room and dining room. There was a big fireplace of red brick with a Dutch oven at one side, and there were hooked rugs on the floor. On the walls hung compasses and sea charts; and round glass balls — once used to float fishing nets — shone in the windows like big blue and white bubbles. A model of the Captain's first ship, the *Foam Flower*, spread its sails high on the mantelpiece.

In the window hung Jericho, the parrot. Poor Jericho had died a long time ago, before the Cat was so much as born. The Captain had been fond of Jericho, and couldn't bear to think of looking up and not seeing him in his place. So Jericho was stuffed and there he still hung in his cage. Once a week Susannah opened the door of the cage and took Jericho out and carefully dusted him.

Susannah kept all the brass in the room shining brightly — the Captain was very particular about that. But neither the Captain nor Susannah noticed that sometimes a few crumbs were left under the table. Only the Cat knew this.

When the Captain sat down and lit his pipe, the Cat sat down, too; but instead of jumping into his chair opposite the Captain, he sat on the floor and watched the crumbs. It was very still except for the tick-tock-ticking of the cuckoo clock, and the steps of Susannah, who was getting supper ready in the kitchen.

The Cat never stirred. After a long while, something moved along the edge of the floor; something ran out on the carpet; something began to nibble a crumb. Before you could have said, "Jack Robinson!" the Cat had that mouse by the neck.

The door into the kitchen was open a little; so in walked the Cat carrying the mouse. He went to Susannah and dropped the mouse carefully right on her foot. Some cats think that a mouse makes a nice present for the person they love, but this cat *knew* how Susannah felt about mice. He knew she was terribly afraid of them.

"Help! Fire! Murder! Police!" yelled Susannah, climbing onto a kitchen chair as fast as she could scramble.

"Why, what's the trouble?" asked the Captain, stumping into the kitchen in a great hurry.

"He's climbin' up the chair!" yelled Susannah. "He's climbin' up the chair! Help!"

The mouse was far wiser than that. He had run back to his hole like lightning. But the Captain had to look under the chair, and

on the chair back, and then take a candle and hunt in all the corners of the kitchen before Susannah would come down. Even then she was very much upset. Said she to the Captain, "Boss, if I had a cat like that one, I wouldn't have him long!" and she began singing:

> "I've known a heap of bad cats,
> But he's the worst I've known.
> If he was mine, I'd take him to the garden
> And bury him like a bone —
> Like a bone, like a bone, like a wicked old bone!"

"He's really a good cat at heart," said the Captain sadly, for he always wanted the Cat and Susannah to be friends. He couldn't understand why they didn't get on better and he scolded the Cat a little when they sat in their chairs by the fire.

But the Cat treated the whole thing as an accident, and he stretched his paws and looked at the Captain with big sleepy eyes and purred to himself as he listened to Susannah singing crossly in the kitchen.

— ELIZABETH COATSWORTH (*Adapted*).

Yes or No?

Write on a paper the numbers from 1 to 15. Read the sentences on this page and on page 62. If a sentence agrees with the story, write *Yes* on the paper after its number. If a sentence does not agree with the story, write *No* on the paper after its number.

1. The Cat lived with the Captain.
2. The Captain's married daughter kept house for him.
3. Susannah was the Captain's niece.
4. The Cat wanted to get into the house.
5. He climbed up a laurel bush and looked in through a window.
6. Susannah was making pies in the kitchen.
7. She came to the door and let the Cat in out of the rain.
8. The Captain came home carrying a big umbrella.
9. The Captain and the Cat went into the living room.
10. Jericho took the Captain's umbrella from his hand.
11. There were some crumbs under the table in the living room.

12. Susannah had left the crumbs for the Cat.

13. The Cat caught a mouse under the kitchen table.

14. The Cat took the mouse to Susannah and dropped it on her foot.

15. Susannah was pleased, as she was very fond of mice.

Things to Do

1. If you want to find out how Susannah and the Cat finally became friends you should read *The Cat and the Captain* by Elizabeth Coatsworth, the book from which the story "The Cat and Susannah" is taken. Miss Coatsworth has written another fine story about a cat, also. It is named *The Cat Who Went to Heaven.*

If you want to know how to take good care of a cat or of any other pet, read *All about Pets,* by Margery Williams Bianco.

2. If you have a cat, tell or write what you do to keep it well and happy. If you have no cat, tell what you would do if you had one.

3. How many different kinds of cats do you know? You might collect pictures of the different kinds and try to find out something about each kind. Cats are very interesting animals, and a great deal has been written about them.

THE RABBIT

When they said the time to hide was mine,
I hid back under a thick grapevine.

And while I was still for the time to pass,
A little gray thing came out of the grass.

He hopped his way through the melon bed
And sat down close by a cabbage head.

He sat down close where I could see,
And his big still eyes looked hard at me,

His big eyes bursting out of the rim,
And I looked back very hard at him.

— ELIZABETH MADOX ROBERTS.

Using the Table of Contents

Write on a paper the numbers from 1 to 10. Look at the Table of Contents on Pages v–viii of your book. Then write the answer to each of these questions after the number of the question on your paper. Get all your answers from the Table of Contents.

1. On what page of the Table of Contents do you find the name of the poem "The Rabbit"?
2. On what page in your book does the story "Whistling Wejack" begin?
3. On what page does a story about a goose begin?
4. On what page does a story about pirates begin?
5. What story begins on page 51?
6. What story begins on page 281?
7. Who wrote the story named "The Golden Touch"?
8. Who wrote "The Princess Who Laughed Too Much"?
9. Find the name of a story written by Clarence Hawkes.
10. Find a title that sounds as if the story would be one you would like.

II

SCHOOLS OF LONG AGO

BOOKS NEVER TELL *

Books never tell
Whether George Washington liked to spell
Or not, or read his readers well,
Or did his home work every day —

* Reprinted by permission from *For Days and Days*, by Annette Wynne. Copyright, 1919, by Frederick A. Stokes Company.

The very way
The teacher tells us to;
I wonder if he liked to do
The hundred things they say we should,
And did they always mark him "good"
Upon the card they gave at school?
I think he never broke a rule,
Or history would tell us so;
For every one would like to know
About the boy who came to be the grand
Great father of our native land.

I find no matter how I try,
Just this — "He never told a lie."
It does *not* say he always wore a tie,
And came to school with jacket neat,
Or sat up straight upon his seat
And never gave a roguish look
And kept his eyes upon his book;
But it's as plain as nose and chin
The perfect boy he must have been!

— ANNETTE WYNNE.

SCHOOLS OF LONG AGO

You have read about the Pilgrims and other early settlers in America. You know what a hard struggle they had, making homes for themselves in a new wild country.

At first they had to spend all their time getting food, finding places to live, and keeping peace with the Indians. After a time, however, they began to worry because there were no schools. How would their children learn to read and write and use figures?

A woman in Plymouth, Massachusetts, where the Pilgrims lived, started a little school in her house. Small children were sent to her to learn. While the children were studying she would spin and knit. Often she had to interrupt a lesson to stir or turn something that was cooking over the open fire.

But, somehow, she taught the children to read and write and to do simple examples in arithmetic. The little girls also learned to sew.

Each little girl, in those early days, had to make a sampler as part of her work in sewing. A sampler was a square of linen with letters and figures embroidered on it in colors. Even a very simple sampler was not complete till it had on it all the letters of the alphabet, the figures, the name of the little girl who made it, and the year.

Some of the samplers had poetry and pictures on them, too. The poetry was usually very serious. One sampler, made by a little girl nine years old, has these lines on it:

> When I was young and in my prime,
> You see how well I spent my time.
> And by my sampler you may see
> What care my parents took of me.

Perhaps you have seen a sampler that has been kept carefully by the descendants of the little

girl who made it. You will find a picture of a sampler on page 79 and a poem about it.

After a time there were a good many schools like the little one in Plymouth. They were called " Dame Schools." The parents of the children paid the woman who taught them. There was very little money in those days, so they often paid her by giving her meat or vegetables or some wood for her fire.

Later, schoolhouses were built. The people who lived in the section around the school helped to build it. They joined together to pay the teacher. In some places, the village church was used for a school on week days.

The first school buildings were made of logs. They had oiled paper for windows. There was a fireplace at one end of the room. Each man who sent a child to school had to send some wood for the fireplace. There was plenty of wood in those days, for the country was covered with forests.

Sometimes when a man did not send his share of wood to the school, his children were sent home. If they were not sent home, they were made to sit in the seats farthest from the fireplace.

There were not many books. An odd little reader called *The New England Primer* was much used for teaching children to read. It had many little black and white pictures. There were rhymes to help teach each letter of the alphabet. For teaching the letter *c*, the rhyme was,

> The Cat will play
> And after slay.

And for *d*,

> The Dog will bite
> A Thief at night.

Very little children often had horn books from which to learn the alphabet. The horn book was not really a book at all. It held a sheet of paper with the alphabet and the Lord's Prayer printed on it. The paper was fastened to an oblong piece of board and the printing was covered with a thin sheet of horn. A strip of brass held the horn and board together. A child could see through the sheet of horn and so study his alphabet without wearing out the paper. Sometimes the board had a short wooden handle. The whole thing looked a little like a small hand mirror with an oblong glass. Often a careful mother would put a string through the handle of the horn book and hang it around her child's neck so that he would not lose it.

Pens were made from goose quills. The teacher had to spend a good deal of time sharpening quills for the pupils. Ink was prepared at home by mixing ink-powder with water. People who could not get ink-powder sometimes made ink from swamp-maple bark, but this was not very good ink.

Paper was scarce and expensive; so the children sometimes wrote on white birch bark or on flat pieces of wood. There were no lead pencils. Slates and slate pencils were not used until later.

As time went on there were more schools and they were built better, but they would not seem very pleasant places to the boys and girls of to-day. The school day was a long one, lasting from eight in the morning until four or five in the afternoon. The teachers often knew little more than the pupils. They were sometimes unkind and cruel. Children who did not study or who were mischievous were often whipped severely.

Life was not very pleasant for the teachers, either. About the time when George Washington was president, a man teacher's pay was ten or twelve dollars a month. Women teachers were not paid so much. In one town in Connecticut, some old record books show that one woman teacher was paid sixty-seven cents a week.

The teachers — unless they taught in their home towns — lived by "boarding round." That is, a teacher lived one week in the home of one pupil and another week in the home of another. This meant that sometimes he had a pleasant home one week and a very uncomfortable one the next. One young man who was "boarding round" wrote to his sister: "I had to wash my face and hands in the brook this morning. When I woke, I found that Mrs. Peller had taken my wash basin and was making the pancakes for breakfast in it."

As time went on, schools grew better. Boys and girls, and teachers too, were more kindly treated. But the greatest changes have come in recent years.

The story "Great-Grandfather's School Days," on page 80, tells about a country school of about seventy-five years ago.

— Jean Y. Ayer.

Which Is Right?

Write on a paper the numbers from 1 to 15. Choose the best word to finish each sentence and write it on your paper after the number of the sentence.

1. At first the Pilgrims had to spend much of their time getting
   books, money, food.
2. They began to worry because there were no
   stores, schools, banks.
3. A woman started a school in her
   house, barn, garage.
4. Each little girl had to make a
   sampler, dress, pudding.
5. The first school buildings were made from
   bricks, stone, logs.
6. The windows were made from
   cloth, paper, leather.
7. The schoolroom was heated by a
   stove, furnace, fireplace.
8. In the old schools, there were few
   children, teachers, books.
9. Little children often had horn books from which to learn
   geography, arithmetic, the alphabet.

10. Every man who sent a child to school had to supply some

coal, wood, gasoline.

11. In some places children went to school in the village

store, park, church.

12. The children wrote with

fountain pens, quill pens, pencils.

13. The school day began at

eight, nine, ten.

14. Children who did not study were often

praised, helped, whipped.

15. As time went on, schools grew

worse, better, smaller.

Things to Do

1. You can read more about old schools in *Work and Play in Colonial Days*, by Mary H. MacElroy, and in *The Puritan Twins*, by Lucy Fitch Perkins.

2. It would be interesting to play some afternoon that your school is one of the schools of long ago. Perhaps some of you can find at home and bring to school, for an exhibit, some old schoolbooks, a horn inkwell, a quill pen, a sampler, or other things that might have been in an old-time school.

THE SAMPLER

When great-grandmother was ten years old,
They gave her a needle and colored thread —
Blue and crimson and white and gold —
And "Start on your sampler now," they said.
And day by day as her elders planned,
Letter by letter in red and gold,
She set her stitches with careful hand —
When great-grandmother was ten years old.

Maybe 'twas different in her day,
For never a leaf is on a tree,
While the birds sit up in the queerest way,
Straight in the air, quite easily.
I've thought and thought, but I'm sure I never
Ate any such fruit as her baskets hold.
My! little girls were surely clever
When great-grandmother was ten years old!

— NANCY BYRD TURNER.

ABCDEF
GHIJKL
MNOPQ
RSTUV
WXYZ
abcdefgh
ijklmnop
qrstuvw
xyz 12
3456789
A diligent Scholar is an ornament to a School
Phoebe Ann Dawson
Aged 10 years May
1845

GREAT-GRANDFATHER'S SCHOOL DAYS

Great-Grandfather Warren had come to make a visit. Ted and Anne were delighted. They were very fond of their great-grandfather. He was a bright, merry person in spite of being almost eighty years old, and he always had interesting stories to tell.

The children called him "Greatest." That was partly because it was a shorter name than "great-grandfather" and partly to show that they thought Mr. Warren a splendid person, as, indeed, he was.

"We're going to have a swimming pool in our new school," said Ted, as soon as Great-Grandfather was seated comfortably and all ready for a talk.

"Have what?" said Great-Grandfather in a surprised voice.

"A swimming pool," said Ted, "and a place to play basket ball, and an athletic field, and — "

"My class is going to have cooking lessons," said Anne. "The new school has the nicest kitchen I ever saw. I shall be *so* glad when we can move in."

"It seems strange to me," said Great-Grandfather, "to think of all those things in a school. But I am glad you have them. I learned to swim in a river and my mother taught my sisters to cook. How everyone would have laughed when I was a boy at the idea of learning to swim in school or to cook, either!"

"How many rooms did your school have, Greatest?" asked Anne.

"Just one room," said Great-Grandfather.

"One room!" said Ted. "Where were the other grades?"

"All the grades were in that one room," replied Great-Grandfather. "When I first

went to school, I was five years old. There were some boys and girls in the school seventeen or eighteen years old and of all the ages between. There were about thirty children in the school, and one teacher taught us all.

"I lived in a small town. It was divided into parts called 'districts.' There was one school for each district and one teacher for each school."

"Are there any schools like that now?" asked Ted.

"Oh, yes," replied Great-grandfather. "There are a good many, but they are better than the school I went to. They have more comfortable desks and seats, more books and other things, and better-trained teachers.

"Our school was old even when I went to it. My father had gone to it when he was a boy. It was built of brick; so it had lasted pretty well.

"When we came to school in the morning, we went first into a small room, called an 'entry,' where we hung our hats and coats. Wood was stacked up at one end of the entry. This was to burn in the stove that kept the school warm in winter.

"In one corner of the entry was a low shelf. A water pail stood on this shelf and a dipper hung beside the water pail. A child who wanted a drink dipped the dipper into the pail and drank out of the dipper."

“Weren’t you afraid of germs?” asked Anne.

“I had never heard of germs at that time,” said Great-Grandfather. “I suppose I must have met a good many, though, without being introduced.

“In the morning, we all played outside until the teacher came to the door and rang a bell. Then we went inside. We hung up our caps and coats and went to our seats.

“There was no real playground, but no one seemed to mind our playing on the land around the school, and we sometimes played in the sandy road in front. People came along occasionally, driving horses or oxen, but we didn’t have to dodge automobiles in those days.

“But let us go back to the schoolroom. It was a long room. At one end was a big desk for the teacher and an armchair. The teacher’s desk stood on a platform about six or eight inches high. Around the other three sides of the room, there was a shelf about three feet from the floor. The shelf sloped down a little from the wall. Long benches without any backs faced the shelf.

"The older boys and girls sat on these benches and used the sloping shelf for a desk top. There was a narrower straight shelf under the sloping one where we could keep our books and slates and slate pencils.

"Behind the benches where the bigger boys and girls sat, was another row of lower benches without desks. These were for the little boys and girls. As the benches had no backs, school was a pretty tiresome place for small children.

"There was a square stove in the middle of the room. Wood was burned in it. If you sat near the stove in winter, you were usually too warm. If you sat far away from it, you were sure to be too cold. We usually thought, though, that being too warm was better than being too cold.

" There were windows on both sides of the school; so the room was quite light. But no one worried then about what direction the light came from.

" When the teacher wanted any class to recite, the boys and girls in that class came to the open space in the middle of the room. They all stood in a straight line lengthways of the room with their toes touching a crack in the floor. If the class was large, the boys and girls stood in two lines facing each other. Sometimes the teacher called on one pupil after another, as they stood in line. Sometimes he skipped around.

" We had one teacher who always asked the questions in order just as they came in the book. He always called on the children in order too. One boy in the class used to count the questions and study only those that he would be called on to answer.

" One day, in the geography class, the teacher skipped a question when he came to

this boy. Instead of asking 'What are the principal products of Venezuela?' he asked 'For what are the ladies of Brazil noted?' This was the next question and the answer was 'For their beauty.' Poor Hiram didn't stop to think, and answered at once, 'Tallow, hides, and horn.'"

"Did you have nice teachers, Greatest?" asked Anne, when she had stopped laughing.

"Well," said Great-Grandfather, "some were very good and some were not so good. The young men and women who taught us were often trying to make some money in order to get ready to do something else than teach. We had a great many different teachers. We usually had a man teacher in winter and a woman teacher at other times."

"Why was that?" asked Ted.

"The big boys worked on the farms in warm weather and went to school in winter. Some of them thought it was fun to act badly in school. So people thought they had to have a man teacher in winter so that he could whip the big boys if they were too troublesome."

"Did you ever get a whipping, Greatest?" asked Ted.

"Yes, once or twice," said Great-Grandfather. "I remember one time especially. I wanted to go to a wedding. One of my aunts was going to be married. There was to be a good deal of company and I knew there would be a fine supper. We needed to start early in order to get to my grandfather's house in time for the wedding. Father said I wasn't to go, as he didn't want me to stay out of school.

"That morning I went to school very early. Another boy and I climbed up on the roof of the school and put a heavy piece of board over the top of the chimney. Of course, when the fire was started in the stove, the room filled with smoke and the children had to be dismissed."

"Did you go to the wedding?" asked Ted.

"Yes, I did," said Great-Grandfather, "and I had a splendid supper and two helpings of everything; but the next day a man who had seen me on the school roof told my father and the teacher. I had a whipping at school and one at home, too."

"Were you very sorry about being so bad?" asked Anne.

" Well, I'm sure I ought to have been," said Great-Grandfather.

" By the time I was a really big boy," he went on, " the school had changed a good deal. The old desks and seats were taken out and seats more like those you have in school were put in. Each desk and seat, though, was large enough for two children."

" Were you allowed to sit with one of your friends? " asked Anne.

" Yes, if you didn't do too much whispering," said Great-Grandfather. " If a boy was troublesome, the teacher sometimes made him go and sit with a girl. We didn't like that because everybody always laughed."

Great-Grandfather stopped, as though the story were ended.

" Please tell us some more about your school," said Ted.

" I think dinner is ready," said Great-Grandfather, " and I am almost as fond of good things to eat now as I was when I went to my aunt's wedding. I'll tell you more after dinner."

— JEAN Y. AYER.

YES OR NO?

Write on a paper the numbers from 1 to 20. Read the sentences on pages 92–93. If a sentence tells something that Great-Grandfather Warren told, write *Yes* on your paper after the number of that sentence. If a sentence tells something that he did not tell, write *No*.

1. I learned to swim in a river.

2. My sisters learned to cook at school.

3. The school I went to had ten rooms.

4. I first went to school when I was five years old.

5. The town in which I lived was divided into parts called "districts."

6. There was one school in each district.

7. There were about eighty children in the school.

8. The school I went to was built of logs.

9. The teacher's desk stood on a platform.

10. The little boys and girls had no desks.

11. The room was heated by a large fireplace.

12. Coal was used for heating the school.

13. A great many automobiles passed the school every day.

14. The big boys went to school only in winter.

15. Father let me stay away from school whenever I wanted to.

16. We usually had a woman teacher in the winter.

17. I was never whipped in school.

18. We had the same teacher for many years.

19. At school, we all drank water from the same dipper.

20. At that time, I was very much afraid of germs.

Things to Do

1. A good story for you to read that tells about children in a school like the one Great-Grandfather Warren went to is named *The Hoosier Schoolboy*. It is by Edward Eggleston.

2. Arrange each of these lists of words in alphabetic order. You will have to skip some letters. In your first column, the first word will be *clover* and the second word will be *dodge*.

roguish	meadow	grades
jacket	frolic	built
visit	vegetable	dipper
dodge	calendar	class
mound	plump	small
yelled	dandelion	tiresome
tunnel	lazy	crack
clover	abroad	questions
wedding	brick	merry
geography	splendid	platform

A LETTER FROM A PIONEER

Look at a map of the United States and find the states between the Mississippi River, the Ohio River, and the Great Lakes. Perhaps you live in one of those states.

Before this part of our country was divided into states, it was called the Northwest Territory. People from Massachusetts and New York and from other eastern states went out to the Northwest Territory and made homes there.

These travelers went in covered wagons, for there were no railroads. They had to meet unfriendly Indians and wild animals. They were brave or they would not have dared to go. We call them *pioneers*, because a pioneer is a person who makes a way for others to follow.

Here is a letter that was written by a young woman who went with her husband to live in the Northwest Territory. She wrote the letter to her brother — a boy in Connecticut.

March 1, 1835.

Dear Richard:

Although I was up very early this morning, I am sitting up to write this letter, for I want it to go in the mail that leaves to-morrow.

You would laugh if you could see my lamp. It is made from clay in the shape of a shallow bowl and is filled with bear's oil. There is a little groove on one side of the bowl. The part of the wick that is not in the oil lies in this groove. The wick is made from cotton that grew in Eliza Hardin's garden. She didn't have much luck with her cotton, but she did save enough for lamp wicks. It is too cold here for raising cotton.

You wanted to know what kind of school the children go to. I will tell you about that.

We didn't find much of a school here when we came; so Henry started to see what he could do about having a better one. He said he would give an acre of ground if the other farmers would help put up the building.

The men who had children were glad to help. Several gave logs and boards, others gave nails, and a great many helped to get the ground ready and put up the building. The boat-store man gave a broom and a water bucket.

The building is tight and warm and the cracks are well chinked. There is a big fireplace at one end of the room. The benches and desks are built around the walls of the room, but on cold days the children sit on slabs of wood near the fireplace.

This winter, Elder Cox, our minister, is teaching the school. We pay him a dollar and a quarter for each child.

The greatest trouble was to find books. When we had collected all there were in the neighborhood, we found that the *Life of Washington*, *Robinson Crusoe*, the *Pilgrim's Progress*, and the *Bible* were about all we could get. Our only real schoolbooks are McGuffey's *Speller* and Dayball's *Arithmetic*.

Elder Cox is a fine penman. I wish you could see the copies he sets for William. We mothers make copy books of foolscap paper. We fold the sheets to make leaves and sew the leaves together. We make ink by soaking oak galls in vinegar.

Henry made William and Dick an inkwell by cutting a section of a cow's horn and putting a flat wooden stopper in the bottom. Now all the boys have them.

The children have rulers made of wood. We fasten to the end of the ruler a piece of lead made by melting the lead and running it into a wooden mold. A hole is drilled in one end of the lead so it can be tied to the ruler by a string. The other end of the lead is sharpened for writing. I wish we had some lead pencils like those you wrote about.

One of the nicest things the Elder teaches is good manners. The boys have to bow when they come into the schoolroom and the girls have to curtsey. The boys are not allowed to come into the room with their hats on. I am very much pleased about this. I want my boys to have good manners even though they are growing up in a new, rough country.

Though Elder Cox is very strict in all his rules, he seldom whips the children. The schoolmaster we had last year seemed to think he wasn't doing his duty unless he whipped some one every day. He had the children all

study aloud, too; so you can imagine what a noisy place the schoolroom was. Of course having children study aloud is an old-fashioned idea.

The children play outside the school until the teacher comes. Then they go in and take their seats. When the Elder says "Books, books!" they are all in order and ready to study. The boys sit on one side of the room and the girls on the other, just as we used to at home.

We had a woman teacher in the summer. She was a very prim, proper person and had some sayings that amused the children. When little Dick did not read loudly enough, she would say, " Do not read like a mouse in a cheese." At last he said one day, "*Mice* can't read." The teacher thought he was saucy; but he really did not mean to be.

One day, while this teacher had the school, something extremely startling happened. The father of one of the boys had come to the school to leave some lunch for his son. While he was there, his dog chased a young panther up a tree. The man shot the animal and dragged it over to the schoolhouse door. He told his son to bring it home that night so that they could save the skin.

Shortly after school opened for the afternoon, the teacher and children heard an awful scream. The mother panther had come out of the woods and found the body of her dead kitten.

The teacher closed the school door quickly, bolted it, and put a heavy bench against it. When the panther was sure her kitten was dead, she made a rush at the schoolhouse. She ran around it several times. Then she leaped on the roof and began tearing at the boards and running back and forth.

Finding that she could not get inside, she screamed again and her mate appeared. The two went to the dead kitten and looked it over. Then both made a rush for the building, and for half an hour they ran around it and climbed over it. All the time they kept up a screaming that the pupils and their teacher will never forget.

In time the sound was heard by some hunters. They came with their dogs, chased the panthers up a tree, and killed both.

Dick wasn't in school that day, but William was. You can imagine how I felt when he came home and told me what had been happening.

Panthers are growing scarcer in these parts, I am glad to say. They are very dangerous animals. A man who has had a meeting with one and lived to tell about it is something of a hero with us. Dogs are a great help in keeping them off. They are afraid of even a small dog. This is odd because a panther can kill a dog easily, if he tries.

I must stop writing. My lamp is almost burned out.

Please give my love to all the family.

Your affectionate sister,
Polly

— Stella Humphrey Nida (*Adapted*).

Do You Remember?

Copy on paper the numbers written below. Then write on your paper after each number a statement about the word that goes with that number. Your statements must tell things that are told in "A Letter from a Pioneer." For example, 1. *The Northwest Territory was near the Great Lakes.*

1. The Northwest Territory . . .
2. Pioneers . . . .
3. Indians . . . .
4. Covered wagons . . . . . .
5. Railroads . . . .
6. Cotton . . . .
7. Bear's oil . . . .

8. Schoolbooks . . . .
9. Oak galls . . . .
10. William . . . .
11. Elder Cox . . . .
12. Dick . . . .
13. Panthers . . . .
14. Hunters . . . .
15. Dogs . . . .

Things to Do

1. Polly's letter is taken from a book named *Letters of Polly the Pioneer*. It is by Stella H. Nida. Perhaps you will like to read some of the other letters. You can read more about pioneers and about panthers, too, in *Old Settler Stories*, by Mabel E. Fletcher.

2. Here are a column of words and a column of meanings, or definitions. Copy the words and meanings. Put each meaning with the word with which it belongs.

1. pioneer	part of a lamp
2. quill	a sour liquid
3. scream	one who leads the way
4. section	a feather
5. vinegar	a part
6. wick	a loud cry

III
FOR FUN

GOING TOO FAR

A woman who lived in Holland, of old,
Polished her brass till it shone like gold.
She washed her pig after all his meals
In spite of his energetic squeals.
She scrubbed her doorstep into the ground,
And the children's faces, pink and round,
She washed so hard that in several cases
She polished their features off their faces —
Which gave them an odd appearance, though
She thought they were really neater so!

Then her passion for cleaning quickly grew,
And she scrubbed and polished the village
through,
Until, to the rage of all the people,
She cleaned the weather-vane off the steeple.
As she looked at the sky one summer's night
She thought that the stars shone out less
bright;
And she said with a sigh, "If I were there,
I'd rub them up till the world should stare."

That night a storm began to brew,
And a wind from the ocean blew and blew
Till, when she came to her door next day
It whisked her up, and blew her away —
Up and up in the air so high
That she vanished, at last, in the stormy sky.
Since then it's said that each twinkling star,
And the big white moon, shine brighter far.
But the neighbors shake their heads in fear
She may rub so hard they will disappear!

— Mildred Howells.

DR. DOLITTLE AND THE PIRATES *

There once lived in a little town called Puddleby-on-the-Marsh a famous doctor named John Dolittle.

He was very fond of animals and spent all his time curing them when they were ill. He could do this much better than most animal-doctors because he had learned to talk with the animals.

He once took a trip to Africa to cure some sick monkeys. He took some of his animal friends with him. When the monkeys were cured, Dr. Dolittle started back home. This story tells about something that happened when Dr. Dolittle and his animal friends were on the way back.

* Reprinted by permission from *The Story of Dr. Dolittle* by Hugh Lofting. Copyright, 1920, by Frederick A. Stokes Company.

1. Red Sails and Blue Wings

Sailing homeward, the Doctor's ship had to pass the coast of Barbary. This coast is the seashore of the Great Desert. It is a wild, lonely place — all sand and stones. And it was here that the Barbary pirates lived.

These pirates, a bad lot of men, used to wait for sailors to be shipwrecked on their shores. Often, if they saw a boat passing, they would come out in their fast sailing-ships and chase it. When they caught a boat like this at sea, they would steal everything on it. After they had taken the people off they would sink the ship and sail back to Barbary singing songs and feeling proud of the mischief they had done. Then they used to make the people they had caught write home to their friends for money. If the friends sent no money, the pirates often threw the people into the sea.

Now one sunshiny day the Doctor and

Dab-Dab, the duck, were walking up and down on the ship for exercise. A nice fresh wind was blowing the boat along, and everybody was happy. Presently Dab-Dab saw the sail of another ship a long way behind them on the edge of the sea. It was a red sail.

"I don't like the look of that sail," said Dab-Dab. "I have a feeling it isn't a friendly ship. I am afraid there is trouble coming to us."

Jip, the dog, was lying near taking a nap in the sun. He began to growl and talk in his sleep.

"I smell roast beef cooking," he mumbled — "roast beef with brown gravy over it."

"Good gracious!" cried the Doctor. "What's the matter with the dog? Is he *smelling* in his sleep — as well as talking?"

"I suppose he is," said Dab-Dab. "All dogs can smell in their sleep."

"But what is he smelling?" asked the Doctor. "There is no roast beef cooking on our ship."

"No," said Dab-Dab. "The roast beef must be on that other ship over there."

"But that's ten miles away," said the Doctor. "He couldn't smell that far surely!"

"Oh, yes, he could," said Dab-Dab. "You ask him."

Then Jip, still fast asleep, began to growl again and his lip curled up angrily, showing his clean, white teeth.

"I smell bad men," he growled — "the worst men I ever smelt. I smell trouble. I smell a fight. Woof — oo — WOOF!" Then he barked, loud, and woke himself up with a surprised look on his face.

"See!" cried Dab-Dab. "That boat is nearer now. You can count its three big sails — all red. Whoever it is, they are coming after us. . . . I wonder who they are?"

"They are bad sailors," said Jip; "but their ship is very swift. They are surely the pirates of Barbary."

"Well, we must put up more sails on our boat," said the Doctor, "so we can go faster and get away from them. Run downstairs, Jip, and fetch me all the sails you see."

Jip hurried downstairs and dragged up every sail he could find.

But even when all these were put up on the masts to catch the wind, the boat did not go nearly so fast as the pirates' boat. It kept coming on behind, closer and closer.

“ Our ship is too slow,” said Gub-Gub, the pig. “ Might as well try to win a race in a soup tureen as hope to get away from them in this old barge. Look how near they are now! — You can see the mustaches on the faces of the men — six of them. What are we going to do?”

Then the Doctor asked Dab-Dab to fly up and tell the swallows that pirates were coming after them in a swift ship, and what should he do about it.

When the swallows heard this, a thousand came down to the deck of the Doctor's ship. They told him to unravel some pieces of long rope and make them into a lot of thin strings as quickly as he could. Then the ends of these strings were tied on to the front of the ship; and the swallows took hold of the strings and flew off, pulling the boat along.

Although swallows are not very strong when only a few are by themselves, it is different when a great lot of them are together.

In a moment the Doctor found himself traveling so fast he had to hold his hat on with both hands. He felt as though the ship were flying through the waves.

All the animals on the ship began to laugh and dance about in the rushing air, for when they looked back at the pirates' ship, they could see that it was growing smaller now, instead of bigger. The red sails were being left far, far behind.

2. The Rats' Warning

Dragging a ship through the sea is hard work; and after two or three hours the swallows began to get tired in the wings and short of breath. Then they sent a message down to the Doctor to say that they would have to take a rest soon. They said they would pull the boat over to an island not far off, and hide it in a deep bay till they had got breath to go on.

Presently the Doctor saw the island they

had spoken of. It had a very beautiful, high, green mountain in the middle of it.

The ship sailed safely into the bay, where it could not be seen from the open sea. Then the Doctor said he would get off on to the island to look for water — because there was none left to drink on his ship. He told all the animals to get out, too, and play on the grass to stretch their legs.

Now as they were getting off, the Doctor noticed that a whole lot of rats were coming up from downstairs and leaving the ship. Jip started to run after them, because chasing rats had always been his favorite game. But the Doctor told him to stop.

One big black rat seemed to want to say something to the Doctor. He crept forward timidly along the rail, watching the dog out of the corner of his eye. After he had coughed two or three times, and cleaned his whiskers and wiped his mouth, he said, "Ahem — er — you know of course that all ships have rats in them, Doctor, do you not?"

The Doctor said, "Yes."

"And you have heard that rats always leave a sinking ship?"

"Yes," said the Doctor — "so I've been told."

"People," said the rat, "always speak of it with a sneer — as though it were something disgraceful. But you can't blame us, can you? After all, who *would* stay on a sinking ship, if he could get off it?"

"Any one would want to get off," said the Doctor. "Was there — was there anything else you wished to say?"

"Yes," said the rat. "I've come to tell you that we are leaving this one. But we wanted to warn you before we go. This is a bad ship you have here. It isn't safe. The sides aren't strong enough. Its boards are rotten. Before to-morrow night it will sink to the bottom of the sea."

"But how do you know?" asked the Doctor.

"We always know," answered the rat. "The tips of our tails get that tingly feeling — like when your foot's asleep. This morning, at six o'clock, while I was getting breakfast, my tail suddenly began to tingle. At first I thought it was my rheumatism coming back. So I went and asked my aunt how she felt — you remember her? — the long, skinny rat, who came to see you in Puddleby last spring with jaundice? Well — she said *her* tail was tingling like everything! Then we knew, for sure, that this boat was going to sink in less than two days; and we all made up our minds to leave it as soon as we got near enough to any land. It's a bad ship, Doctor. Don't sail in it any more, or you'll surely be drowned. Good-by! We are now going to look on this island for a good place to live."

"Good-by!" said the Doctor; "and thank you very much for coming to tell me. Very kind of you — very! Give my regards to your aunt. I remember her perfectly. . . . Leave that rat alone, Jip! Come here! Lie down!"

Then the Doctor and all his animals went off, carrying pails and saucepans, to look for water on the island, while the swallows took their rest.

"I wonder what is the name of this island," said the Doctor. "It seems a pleasant place. What a lot of birds there are!"

" Why, these are the Canary Islands," said Dab-Dab. " Don't you hear the canaries singing? "

The Doctor stopped and listened.

" Why, to be sure — of course! " he said. " How stupid of me! I wonder if they can tell us where to find water."

Presently the canaries, who had heard all about Dr. Dolittle from other birds, came and led him to a beautiful spring of cool, clear water where the canaries used to take their bath; and they showed him meadows where bird-seed grew and all the other sights of their island. Gub-Gub, the pig, squeaked for joy when he found a whole valley full of wild sugar-cane.

A little later, they had all had plenty to eat and drink, and were lying on their backs while the canaries sang for them. But two of the swallows came hurrying up, very much flustered and excited.

"Doctor!" they cried, "the pirates have come into the bay; and they've all got on your ship. They are downstairs in it looking for things to steal. They have left their own ship with nobody on it. If you hurry and come down to the shore, you can get onto their ship — which is very fast — and escape. But you'll have to hurry."

"That's a good idea," said the Doctor — "splendid!"

He called his animals together at once, said good-by to the canaries, and ran down to the beach.

When they reached the shore, they saw the pirate ship, with the three red sails, standing in the water. Just as the swallows had said — there was nobody on it. All the pirates were downstairs in the Doctor's ship, looking for things to steal.

So Dr. Dolittle told his animals to walk very softly and they all crept onto the pirate ship.

3. The Barbary Dragon

Everything would have gone all right if the pig had not caught a cold in his head while eating the damp sugar-cane on the island. This is what happened:

After they had pulled up the anchor without a sound, and were moving the ship very, very carefully out of the bay, Gub-Gub suddenly sneezed so loud that the pirates on the other ship came rushing upstairs to see what the noise was.

As soon as they saw that the Doctor was escaping, they sailed the other boat right across the entrance to the bay so that the Doctor could not get out into the open sea.

Then the leader of these bad men (who called himself "Ben Ali, the Dragon") shook his fist at the Doctor and shouted across the water.

"Ha! Ha! You are caught, my fine friend! You were going to run off in my ship, eh? But you are not a good enough sailor to beat Ben Ali, the Barbary Dragon. I want that duck you've got — and the pig too. We'll have pork chops and roast duck for supper to-night. And before I let you go home, you must make your friends send me a trunk full of gold."

Poor Gub-Gub began to weep; and Dab-Dab made ready to fly to save her life. But the owl, Too-Too, whispered to the Doctor:

" Keep him talking, Doctor. Be pleasant to him. Our old ship is bound to sink soon — the rats said it would be at the bottom of the sea before to-morrow night — and the rats are never wrong. Be pleasant, till the ship sinks under him. Keep him talking."

" What, until to-morrow night!" said the Doctor. " Well, I'll do my best. . . . Let me see — What shall I talk about? "

" Oh, let them come on," said Jip. " We can fight the dirty rascals. There are only six of them. Let them come on. I'd love to tell that collie next door, when we get home, that I had bitten a real pirate. Let 'em come. We can fight them."

" But they have pistols and swords," said the Doctor. " No, that would never do. I must talk to him. . . Look here, Ben Ali — "

But before the Doctor could say any more, the pirates began to sail the ship nearer, laughing with glee, and saying one to another, " Who will be the first to catch the pig?" Poor Gub-Gub was dreadfully frightened; Jip kept springing into the air and barking and calling Ben Ali bad names in dog-language.

But presently things seemed to go wrong with the pirates. They stopped laughing and cracking jokes. They looked puzzled. Something was making them uneasy.

Then Ben Ali, staring down at his feet, suddenly bellowed out, "Thunder and lightning! — Men, *the boat's leaking!*"

Then the other pirates peered over the side and saw that the boat was indeed getting lower and lower in the water; and one of them said to Ben Ali, "But surely if this old boat were sinking we should see the rats leaving it."

And Jip shouted across from the other ship, "You great duffers, there are no rats there to leave! They left two hours ago!"

But of course the men did not understand him.

Soon the front end of the ship began to go down and down, faster and faster — till the boat looked almost as though it were standing on its head. The pirates had to cling to the rails and the masts and the ropes and anything to keep from sliding off. Then the sea rushed roaring in through all the windows and the doors. At last the ship plunged right down to the bottom of the sea, making a dreadful gurgling sound; and the six bad men were left bobbing about in the deep water of the bay.

Some of them started to swim for the shores of the island, while the others came and tried to get onto the boat where the Doctor was. But Jip kept snapping at their noses, so they were afraid to climb up the side of the ship.

Then suddenly they all cried out in great fear, "*The sharks!* The sharks are coming! Let us get onto the ship before they eat us! Help, help! — The sharks! The sharks!"

And now the Doctor could see, all over the bay, the backs of big fishes swimming swiftly through the water.

4. The Friendly Sharks

One great shark came near to the ship. Poking his nose out of the water he said to the Doctor, "Are you John Dolittle, the famous animal-doctor?"

"Yes," said Doctor Dolittle. "That is my name."

"Well," said the shark, "we know these pirates are a bad lot — especially Ben Ali. If they are bothering you, we will gladly eat them up for you — and then you won't be troubled any more."

"Thank you," said the Doctor. "This is really most kind. But I don't think it will be necessary to eat them. Don't let any of them reach the shore until I tell you — just keep them swimming about, will you? And please make Ben Ali swim over here so that I may talk to him."

So the shark went off and chased Ben Ali over to the Doctor.

"Listen, Ben Ali," said John Dolittle, leaning over the side. "You have been a very bad man; and I understand that you have killed many people. These good sharks here have just offered to eat you up for me — and it would indeed be a fine thing if the seas were rid of you. But if you will promise to do as I tell you, I will let you go in safety."

"What must I do?" asked the pirate, looking down sideways at the big shark who was smelling his leg under the water.

"You must kill no more people," said the Doctor; "you must stop stealing; you must never sink another ship; you must give up being a pirate altogether."

"But what shall I do then?" asked Ben Ali. "How shall I live?"

"You and all your men must go onto this island and be bird-seed farmers," the Doctor answered. "You must grow bird-seed for the canaries."

The Barbary Dragon turned pale with anger. "*Grow bird-seed!*" he groaned in disgust. "Can't I be a sailor?"

"No," said the Doctor, "you cannot. You have been a sailor long enough — and sent many stout ships and good men to the bottom of the sea. For the rest of your life you must be a peaceful farmer. The shark is waiting. Do not waste any more of his time. Make up your mind."

"Thunder and lightning!" Ben Ali muttered — "*Bird-seed!*" Then he looked down into the water again and saw the great fish smelling his other leg.

"Very well," he said sadly. "We'll be farmers."

"And remember," said the Doctor, "that if you do not keep your promise, if you start killing and stealing again, I shall hear of it, because the canaries will come and tell me. And be very sure that I will find a way to punish you. Now go and be a good farmer and live in peace."

Then the Doctor turned to the big shark and waving his hand he said, "All right. Let them swim safely to the land."

After thanking the sharks again for their kindness, the Doctor and his pets set off once more on their journey. As they now had a good ship, they reached home safely.

— HUGH LOFTING.

YES OR NO?

Write on a paper the numbers from 1 to 20. Read the sentences on this page. If a sentence tells what the story tells, write *Yes* after the number on your paper. If a sentence does not tell what the story tells, write *No* after its number.

I

1. Dr. Dolittle was very fond of animals.
2. He took a trip to Africa to cure some sick lions.
3. On the way home Dr. Dolittle saw a ship with a green sail.
4. Jip, the dog, said he smelled roast beef.
5. The swallows pulled Dr. Dolittle's ship very fast.

II

6. The swallows drew the ship all the way home.

7. The rats decided to leave the ship.

8. Dr. Dolittle and the animals went ashore on the coast of Asia.

9. The pirates started to rob Dr. Dolittle's ship.

10. Dr. Dolittle and his animals took the pirates' ship.

III

11. Gub-Gub, the pig, had rheumatism in his leg.

12. The leader of the pirates was called "The Barbary Alligator."

13. The pirate leader made fun of Dr. Dolittle and his animals.

14. Gub-Gub wanted to fight the pirates, but Jip was afraid.

15. The ship the pirates were on sank, and they had to swim.

IV

16. Some whales came and offered to eat the pirates.

17. Dr. Dolittle told the pirates they would have to stop stealing and stop sinking ships.

18. Ben Ali was very much pleased at the thought of living on land.

19. Dr. Dolittle told the pirates they would have to be farmers and raise bird-seed.

20. Dr. Dolittle and the animals sailed home on the pirates' ship.

Things To Do

1. The story of "Dr. Dolittle and the Pirates" is taken from a book named *The Story of Dr. Dolittle.* The author is Hugh Lofting. You will be sure to like this book if you read it. Mr. Lofting has written a number of other interesting books about Dr. Dolittle. If you want to read more about pirates, try *Buccaneers and Pirates of Our Coast* by Frank R. Stockton.

2. Copy the list of words. Look up the definitions of the words in the "Short Dictionary" on pages 396–408, and write each definition after the word with which it belongs.

anxiety	pirate
Barbary	pistol
disgust	shrieking
dragon	tureen
jaundice	weather-vane

THE PRINCESS WHO LAUGHED TOO MUCH

1. The Princess

There was once a little princess who could not cry.

That wouldn't have mattered very much, but the trouble was that she laughed at everything, often when it was not polite to laugh.

Her parents were very much troubled about it, and they called in a wise old woman in order to get her advice. The wise woman went into the matter thoroughly, and finally told them that if the princess could only once be made to cry, the spell would be broken for ever and she would be like other polite people and would not laugh at the wrong times.

This wasn't particularly helpful, but it gave the king and queen some hope. So they immediately set about the task of making the princess weep. Of course it was rather a difficult matter, because they didn't want to make her really unhappy, and they hardly knew how to begin. Finally they offered a reward of five hundred gold pieces to anybody who should make their daughter cry without doing her any harm.

Wise men came from all over the kingdom to see what they could do, and many things were tried, but all to no purpose.

One of the wise men suggested that she should be shut up in a room by herself and fed on bread and water for a whole week. The queen thought this very cruel, but the king persuaded her to try it. She insisted, however, that at any rate it should be bread and milk.

But every time they came to bring the princess her bowl of bread and milk they found her laughing, and at the end of the week she was still as cheerful as ever.

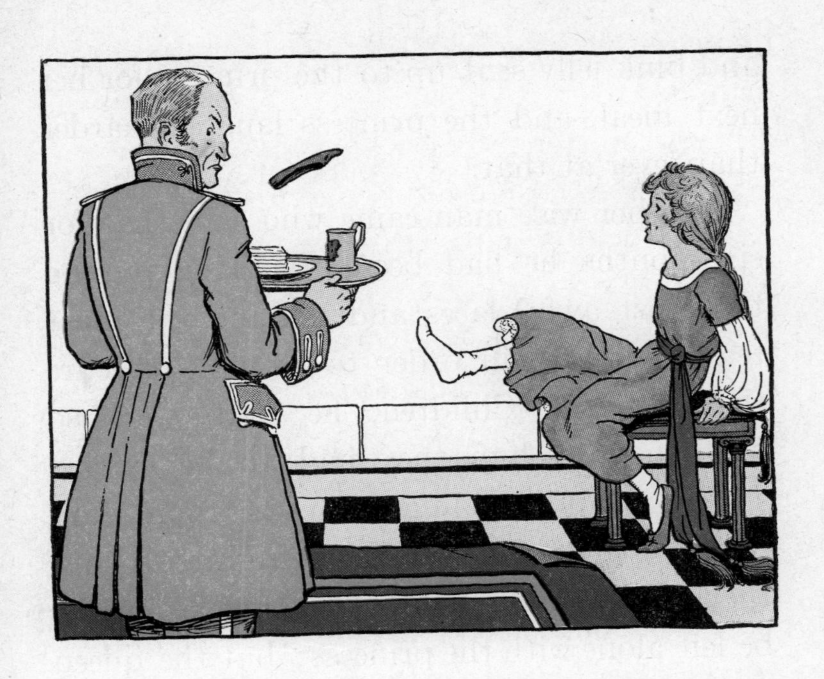

"Look," she said, "my feet have grown so thin that I can't keep my slippers on." Then she kicked her foot into the air and sent her slipper flying across the room, and laughed to see the scandalized face of the butler.

But her mother burst into tears. "My poor starved lamb," she said, "they shall not treat you so any longer." She rushed into the kitchen and ordered soup and chicken and pink jelly sent up to the princess for her next meal, and the princess laughed harder than ever at that.

Another wise man came who said that for six months he had been practicing pulling the most awful faces and making the most terrible noises, in order to be able to cure the princess. Children, he said, were so frightened by him they had to be carried shrieking and howling from the room, and even grown-up people were so frightened that they wept aloud. He asked that he might be left alone with the princess; but the queen waited outside the door.

She trembled with anxiety as she listened, for the noises the wise man made were so blood-curdling that she could hardly bear to hear them herself, and it seemed dreadful that her child should be left alone to endure such a trial.

In a few minutes she heard peals of laughter coming from inside the room, and presently the wise man opened the door. He was quite used up and blue in the face, with the efforts he had been making. "It's no use," he said rather crossly — "no use at all," and he went away looking very cross.

The princess came running out to her mother. "Oh, he *was* a funny man," she said. "Can't he come and do it again?"

Another wise man suggested that all her favorite toys should be broken up. But when he went into the nursery and began smashing her beautiful dolls and playthings, the princess clapped her hands and jumped about and laughed more heartily than ever.

"What fun, what fun!" she said, and she too began throwing the things about. So that plan had to be given up also.

Other wise men came, but as many of their suggestions were cruel and unkind ones, naturally the king and queen would not hear of them; and at last they began to fear that nothing could be done.

2. Marigold

Now in a small village on the borders of the king's great park, there lived a widow with her little daughter, Marigold.

They were very poor. The mother earned what she could by doing odd jobs of washing, sewing, or cleaning for her neighbors. But she fell ill, and poor Marigold was in great trouble, for she had no money to buy comforts for her mother.

Their little savings had to go for food to keep them alive, and every day these grew less and less.

Marigold knew all about the little princess at the castle. She had often heard people speak of her. She had even seen the princess sometimes, riding about the roads on her white pony. One day as she was cooking the noon meal an idea came into her head.

As soon as dinner was over, she put on her hat and cloak and told her mother that she

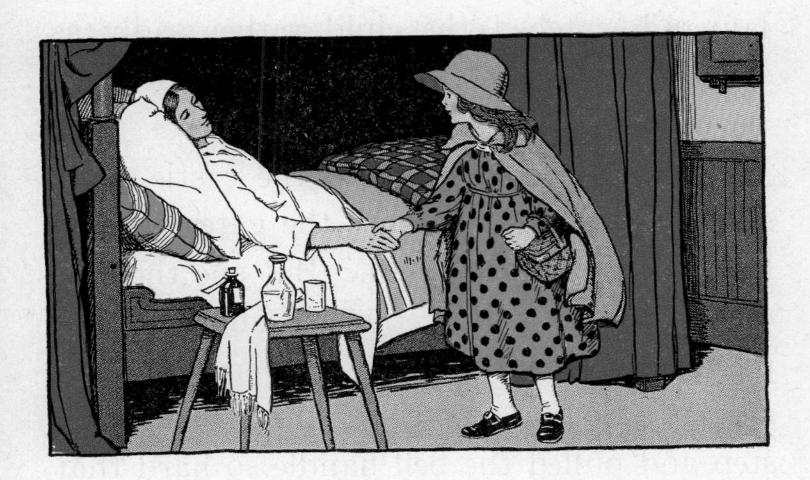

was going to the king's palace to see if she could make the princess cry and so earn the five hundred gold pieces.

Her mother did her best to persuade her not to go.

" How can you hope to succeed," she said, " when so many clever people have tried and failed? You are only my dear little Marigold, and it is useless for you to attempt such a task. Give it up, my child."

But Marigold was determined, and when her mother saw this she said no more, but lay and watched the child rather sadly as she set bravely off for the castle with a little basket over her arm.

When Marigold came to the castle gates she felt frightened because the gates were so big and she was so small. But she thought of her mother and of the five hundred gold pieces that would buy her everything she needed. So she stood on tiptoe on the top step and pulled the bell handle so hard that she was quite frightened at the noise it made.

A very grand footman opened the door. When he saw Marigold standing there in her woollen frock and cloak with her little basket, he said, "Go to the back entrance!" in a loud, cross voice, and shut the door in her face.

So she went round to the back entrance. This time the door was opened by a red-faced kitchen-maid. "We've no food to give away to-day," said the maid, and she too was about to shut the door.

But the queen happened to be in the kitchen giving her orders for the day, and she saw Marigold through the window. She came to the window and called to her.

"What is it, my child?" she asked, as Marigold stood there looking very unhappy.

"I've come to make the princess cry, please Your Majesty," she said, and made a curtsey, for the queen looked very grand with her crown on her head and her lovely ermine train held up over her arm to keep it off the kitchen floor.

When the queen heard what Marigold had come for, she smiled and shook her head. How could a little country girl hope to do what so many wise men had failed to accomplish? But Marigold was so sure that she could make the princess cry that at last the queen agreed to let her see what she could do.

"You won't hurt her?" she said. But she smiled as she said it. Marigold had such a kind little face that she did not look as if she would hurt anyone.

3. A Surprise

Marigold was taken to the princess's rooms. The queen went with her and introduced her and explained why she had come.

The princess was delighted to see a nice little rosy-cheeked girl instead of one of the dull old men who had so often come to visit her. So the queen shut the door and left the little girls alone together.

By this time the news of the little village girl who had come to make the princess cry had spread all over the palace. Soon a crowd of people was waiting outside the door.

"It's nonsense," said the Chamberlain to the Prime Minister. "A mere child! I don't suppose she's ever been outside the village."

"Quite ridiculous!" whispered the ladies-in-waiting to the court pages. "Do you think she knows how to make a correct curtsey?"

At last the king and queen could stand the suspense no longer. They quietly opened the

door and peeped in. And what do you think they saw?

The princess was standing at a table in the middle of the room with Marigold's basket in front of her, peeling onions as hard as she could, while the tears streamed down her face. She was crying at last — and if you have ever tried to peel strong onions, you know why she cried!

The king and queen rushed in and clasped her in their arms, onions and all. The ladies-in-waiting stood with their perfumed handkerchiefs pressed to their noses, the pages tittered, and the cook, who was standing at the bottom of the stairs, muttered to himself when he heard the news, "Well, *I* could have done that."

The Prime Minister rushed about the room with his wig on one side and shook everybody by the hand, exclaiming, "Wonderful, wonderful! And so simple! So very simple! We must send out the news at once. Where are my glasses? Where is my pen?"

So the princess was cured, and from that time she became like everybody else and cried when she was unhappy and laughed when she was glad, though I am pleased to say that she always laughed a great deal more than she cried.

As for Marigold, she got the five hundred gold pieces, of course, and was able to give her mother everything she needed, so that she was soon quite well. The king and queen were most grateful. They invited Marigold to the palace to play with their little daughter, and they loaded her with presents.

Because she was sweet and modest she wasn't spoiled by all this, but grew up charming, kind, and beautiful. I have heard that in the end she married a king's son and that they had an onion for their crest, but I'm not at all sure about that.

— ROSE FYLEMAN (*Adapted*).

SENTENCES TO FINISH

Look at the incomplete sentences on pages 146–147. Then write on a paper the numbers from 1 to 20. Write after each number the words that are needed to finish the sentence that has that number.

I

1. There was once a little princess who —— —— ——.

2. She laughed at everything, even when it was not polite —— ——.

3. Her parents asked the advice of a —— ——.

4. If the princess could cry once, the spell —— —— ——.

5. The king and queen offered a reward of —— —— —— ——.

6. A wise man suggested that the princess should be fed on —— —— ——.

7. The princess said, "My feet have grown so thin, I can't keep —— —— ——."

II

8. A poor widow had a little daughter, whose —— —— ——.

9. Marigold had no money to buy comforts —— —— ——.

10. She knew all about the —— ——.

11. She set out for the castle carrying a —— ——.

12. The queen was in the kitchen and saw Marigold through —— ——.

13. Marigold was sure she could make —— —— ——.

III

14. The queen took Marigold to see —— ——.

15. The news about the little village girl spread all —— —— ——.

16. At last the king and queen opened the door of the princess's room and —— ——.

17. They saw the princess, standing at a table, —— ——.

18. As the princess did this work, tears were streaming —— —— ——.

19. The princess was cured and became like —— ——.

20. The king and queen often invited Marigold to —— ——.

Things to Do

1. If you like the story "The Princess Who Laughed Too Much," you will enjoy reading others in the same book. It is *The Rainbow Cat* by Rose Fyleman. In the book the story is called "The Princess Who Could Not Cry."

2. "The Princess Who Laughed Too Much" is in three parts. Try to think of other names for the three parts that would do as well as those in your book.

3. Each word in the first list below has a word that rhymes with it in the second list and another in the third list. Copy the first list, and write after each word the words from the other lists that rhyme with it. After *better*, you should write *letter* and *setter*, and so on.

1.	better	chest	child
2.	crest	pears	brown
3.	crown	cried	squeal
4.	failed	steal	money
5.	funny	sleep	sailed
6.	meal	hailed	said
7.	smiled	letter	cries
8.	tried	honey	steep
9.	weep	fun	sighed
10.	wise	drown	setter
11.	stairs	eyes	ring
12.	wept	wild	gun
13.	bread	sting	rest
14.	done	head	crept
15.	bring	slept	bears

4. Make a little play from "The Princess Who Laughed Too Much." How many acts will you have? Give each act a name. What parts of the play can be made very funny?

IV
EVERYDAY THINGS

MAGIC

Oh, a bottle of ink, a bottle of ink!
What's bottled up in a bottle of ink?
Princes and ponies and pirates and bees,
Pixies and brownies and magical keys,
Lions and tigers and ladies and knights,
Colorful peeps at most marvelous sights,
Witches and goblins and fairies and fays,
Heroes who lived in the far-away days —
More wonderful things than you ever
could think,
All bottled up in a bottle of ink!

— Blanche Jennings Thompson.

AN INK-BOTTLE STORY

"When I was in Boston last week," said Aunt Lou, "I visited an ink factory."

"When I was fishing last summer," said Daddy, "I *caught* an ink factory."

At this the children all shouted, "O Da-a-a-d!" and "Daddy, you *didn't*" and other things of that sort.

At first Aunt Lou looked surprised. Then she laughed. "Did you really catch one?" she said. "Tell us about it."

"We'll let Aunt Lou tell about her ink factory first," said Dad. "It's a longer story than mine and more important."

"Go ahead, Aunt Lou," said Jack and Jimmy and Joan all together.

"Well," said Aunt Lou, "while I was in Boston, I read some letters that my great-grandmother wrote when she was a young girl. One of the letters was hard to read. The ink was much paler than in the others. In it great-grandmother said that she had not been able to get any ink-powder. So she had made some ink by soaking the bark of swamp maple in water, boiling the water, and adding something called *copperas*.

"In those days, it seems, people made the ink they used. When children went to school, each child had to take his own ink and ink bottle from home. My great-grandmother's ink bottle was made out of part of a cow's horn.

"Reading those old letters started me thinking about ink. So, one day, I went to visit an ink factory.

"A very pleasant man took me over the factory and told me a great deal about ink. If I tell you about it, that will help me to remember what I learned.

"On the top floor of the factory were big tanks. Here the ink was mixed. When the ink is ready, it goes through tubes to very large vats on a floor below. These vats together hold sixty thousand gallons of ink.

"After the ink has been in the vats for a while and has had time to settle, it goes on. It runs through other tubes to the filling machines.

"The bottles are filled, corked, and labelled by machinery. It is fun to see the labelling machines reach up, take down labels, gum these, and then stick them on the bottles.

"After this, the bottles are ready for packing in boxes. When a box is filled, a man puts on the cover and slides the box under a nailing machine. He presses a lever and the nailing machine nails the cover on.

"The boxes are then ready to send out. They go all over the world. They go to Spain and China, to Ireland and the Fiji Islands, and to all the countries in between."

“Does the ink really go to the Fiji Islands, Aunt Lou?” asked Jimmy.

“Yes,” said Aunt Lou. “The man at the factory told me they had some large orders for blue ink from one of the Fiji Islands. They found out, though, that the people on the island weren't writing letters with the ink. They were using it to dye their straw hats.”

“Did the people at the factory make the ink the way your great-grandmother made it?” asked Jack.

“They make some ink in a way quite like that,” said Aunt Lou, “but they don't use maple bark. They use logwood chips. The logwood comes from Central America and the West Indies. People who want ink in large quantities and do not need a very lasting ink buy this kind. The ink you use in school is logwood ink.

“This factory makes several hundred different kinds of ink and makes them in many different ways. Of course they didn't tell me how they made the different kinds. They have to keep their recipes for themselves.

"The ink that lasts the longest without fading is made from nut galls. Those are found on oak and willow trees. A gall fly makes a little hole in the twig of a tree and lays eggs there. This seems to hurt the tree and a lump grows over the spot where the eggs have been laid. These lumps are nut galls. You can find them in the woods.

"The ink is made in some such way as this. The galls are cut from the tree before the young insect comes out. They are crushed and then soaked in water for two or three days. The water is poured off and a chemical called *green vitriol* is added to it. This is the same chemical my great-grandmother called copperas in her letter. This mixture makes ink. A little mucilage is put in so that the ink will not be too thin and a little carbolic acid is added, too. The acid keeps the ink from getting mouldy.

" This kind of ink has been made for hundreds of years. It was in use when Columbus discovered America. Writing that was done with gall ink before Columbus sailed is still clear and easy to read. So you see what good ink it is.

" Secret inks are interesting. They are the kind that do not show on paper till they have been heated or treated in some other special way. Spies sometimes use secret inks in war time so that their messages cannot be read by the enemy. If you want to see how they work, write on a paper with lemon juice and then heat the paper.

" India ink is another old kind — probably the oldest of all. It is made from lamp black — a kind of soot — mixed with glue and water. It also lasts well. Artists use it a great deal to make black and white drawings. Work done in India ink will not blur if water is dropped on it. It is also very hard to erase. This ink is sometimes called China ink. The

Chinese and Japanese use it. They write with small brushes instead of with pens. Indeed their writing is done more like painting than like writing as we know it.

"The colored inks are made with dyes, though some red ink is made from the Brazil-wood tree much as black ink is made from logwood.

"Printer's ink, the kind that is used in printing books and newspapers, has to be thick and quite different from ordinary inks. It is like a kind of dark varnish. A special kind of ink is made for the ribbons in typewriters. It would be hard to name all the kinds."

Aunt Lou stopped. "I think it's your turn now," she said to Dad.

"Oh, yes," cried Joan, "I almost forgot the factory Daddy caught."

"My story isn't as good as Aunt Lou's," said Dad, "but I *did* catch an ink factory.

"One day last summer when we were fishing, we pulled up a fish that seemed to have black

water all around him. When we got him into the boat, we found that we had a cuttle-fish. He is a queer-looking creature with ten arms — or legs — growing out around his head. He walks on these on the bottom of the sea with his head down. He's a little hard to describe, but I can show you a picture of him in the encyclopedia.

"The cuttle-fish has a bag in his body filled with a black fluid like ink. He squirts this out to make the water dark around him so that his enemies can't see him.

"This ink bag can be taken out and the ink dried. It then forms a powder. This powder is used in coloring a brown paint that artists use. The paint is called *sepia.* The powder can also be used to make ink. The old Romans used this kind of ink. Probably the ink-powder that Aunt Lou's great-grandmother used came from a cuttle-fish. And that," said Dad, "is the end of *my* story."

"Thank you, Aunt Lou. Thank you, Daddy," said Joan politely. "I think the ink stories were fine."

"So do I," said Jack.

"If Mother has any lemons," said Jimmy, "I'm going to write a secret letter."

"Then you'll be writing a letter with lemon aid," said Daddy.

The children looked puzzled for a moment.

Then they laughed and shouted, "Oh, *I* see, *I* see," and hurried off to look for lemons.

— Jean Y. Ayer.

Can You Tell?

1. Where did people make ink long ago?
2. Where is ink made to-day?
3. Name five different things from which ink can be made.
4. How many of these are used to-day?
5. How are colored inks made?
6. Name two kinds of ink that do not fade easily.
7. What ink will not run if water is spilled on the writing?
8. What is "secret ink"?
9. What is the ink called that is made from lampblack?
10. What is the coloring called that is made from cuttle-fish powder?

An Outline to Fill

Copy the outline on page 162 and fill in the parts that are left out. Write *Ink* above your outline. Do not write in your book.

I. Ink is made from

1.
2.
3.
4.

II. Inks that last a long time without fading are

1.
2.

III. Inks that artists use are

1.
2.

Things to Do

1. If you would like to read more about ink, you will find a good deal in any encyclopedia that tells about common things. A book that tells about the making of ink, pencils, paper, and other things that we use every day is *Modern Aladdins and Their Magic* by Charles E. Rush and Amy Winslow.

2. Perhaps you would like to try writing a secret letter with lemon juice. Do not plan to write a long letter, for lemon juice does not flow freely. Use a fairly smooth paper and a clean pen. It is easier if you print the letters. Put the paper aside till the lemon juice is dry. When you want to read the letter, iron it with a warm flat iron.

A SOAP STORY

1. Jimmy's Questions

One warm day in spring Jimmy Martin came home from a long hike. His face and hands were so black with dirt that his mother hardly knew him.

But when Jimmy went to wash his hands, he found that there was no soap. He called at once, "Mother, where is the soap?"

"I'm sorry, Jimmy," said his mother. "I ordered some soap to-day, but it hasn't come yet."

"Well, mother, I guess I'll have to eat supper with dirty hands," said Jimmy. "I can't get this dirt off without soap and lots of it."

When Jimmy found that he couldn't get his hands clean, he began to think for the first time about how useful soap is. In a short time the soap came, and he felt as if a friend had arrived. He really enjoyed washing his hands and face.

Later, at the supper table, Jimmy said, "Father, I've been thinking about soap, and I've a lot of questions I'd like to ask."

"All right, son; let's hear them."

"Well, did people always have soap? What would we do if we didn't have any soap at all? What *is* soap, anyway?"

"Wait a minute," said his father, as Jimmy was going on. "Slow up a bit. Those are good questions, but I can't answer them as fast as you can ask them. I have an idea. How would you like to write down those questions you want to ask about soap, and we'll try to answer one or two every night for a while?"

"Fine, Father," said Jimmy. "I'll start that list to-night."

Then Mother Martin spoke, "I'd like to play a soap game right now. Let's see who can name the greatest number of different ways that we have used soap in this house to-day. You begin, Jimmy."

"Soap for baths," said Jimmy, promptly.

"Soap for dishes," said Sue.

"Shaving soap," said father.

"Soap in tooth paste," said mother. "I don't believe any of you thought of that!"

"I washed my dog with soap to-day," said Sister Sue, and they all laughed.

"That's why there wasn't any soap left in the bathroom," said Jimmy.

The next evening Jimmy came to the supper table, carrying a sheet of paper in his hand. He could hardly wait for the family to be seated before he began, "Father, here are just a few questions for you to answer. I told my teacher about our talk last night, and showed her the questions I wrote down. She told the class about it, and every boy and girl had some question to ask, too. They asked about a hundred! So Miss Dean let us work out a shorter list together."

"That's fine," said father. "I'll do my share of answering questions if you'll do yours."

"Now," said mother, "I should like to hear those questions."

"Read them, Jim," said father.

These are some of the questions Jimmy read:

What is soap?
When did people first use it?
How is it made?

How does soap make our hands and clothes clean?
Why does soap foam up and make suds?
Why are there so many kinds of soap?
Is one kind of soap as good as another?
How can we tell what kind is best to buy?

"Thank you, Jimmy," said mother. "I'm sure I'd like to know the answers to those questions. Soap is needed for so many and such different things, like bathing the baby and washing those hiking clothes of yours; and there are so many kinds, sometimes I find it hard to tell which are best to buy."

"Let's have the first questions first," went on mother. "There's ice cream for dessert. We can eat it slowly and listen while father tells us about the time when people first began to use soap."

"Hm-m-m," said father, "that sounds like a fine plan for everybody but me! However, I'll keep my promise. I read a little to-day to be ready for Jim to-night."

"People of long ago," father began, "did not keep themselves as clean as we do to-day, for they did not have our good soaps. How would you like it if, before you went to school each morning, you had to use oil and fine sand instead of a good soapy bath? That is the way Cleopatra is said to have taken her baths, and she was a queen."

"Oh, I know about her," exclaimed Jimmy. "She was queen in Egypt ever so long ago. That big obelisk, like a tall monument, in Central Park in New York is called Cleopatra's Needle. It came from Egypt."

"Did she sew with it?" asked Sue, with a giggle.

"She *was* queen ever so long ago," said father, paying no attention to Miss Sue; "nearly two thousand years ago. But about six hundred years before that, people had something which was used as soap. It is mentioned in the Bible. It was not really soap, but a kind of fine earth or clay. So I suppose people washed for many hundreds of years about as Cleopatra did.

"People washed clothes in those days, as they still do in some parts of the world, by beating them up and down in the water at the edge of a stream or pool. This was hard work, and I don't believe we would have thought the clothes very clean when they were done. Sometimes wash day came only two or three times a year; so it was a great event. The person in charge of washing the clothes in the king's palace and the homes of the nobles had an important position. In Cleopatra's court

he was called the Royal Chief Washer. There is an old poem that gives us a picture of washing in Cleopatra's time:

"The washer, he who washes on the dike,
Neighbor to the crocodile that swims up stream.

" The chief city in the world in those days was Rome. You can find it on your map of Italy. A Roman named Pliny, who lived about that time, was very much interested in what the people did every day and in the things they had in their homes to use. We call him "Pliny the Elder" because he had a young relative also named Pliny. He wrote a book, and it tells that the Romans at that time had something that we may really call soap. They learned from a neighboring people called the Gauls how to make it from goat's tallow and wood ashes."

"I'm glad I don't have to bathe my baby with it," said mother.

"You wouldn't have bathed the baby with it in those days," said father, "if you had been a poor woman. The poorer people did not have soap to use, except sometimes to heal skin diseases.

"Pliny lived near the city of Pompeii, and his habit of looking into everything that was going on around him probably caused his death. There came a big eruption of Mount Vesuvius, a volcano near by. Pompeii was buried deep by the ashes that fell. Pliny went too close and he was buried also. After nineteen hundred years, the ashes were dug away enough to show how the city looked when it was buried, and a soap factory is one of the interesting things that was found.

"For a thousand years or more after Pliny's time there were a good many people who had dirty faces and hands, as well as dirty clothing. For the use of soap did not become common. Then we find that in the south of France more olives were raised than could be eaten or used for olive oil. So a factory was started to make soap from the oil of the unused olives.

"Then, about the time that Columbus discovered America, England began to make soap. It was not very good, and it cost a great deal more than soap costs now."

"People were just beginning to understand how to make quite good soap, cheap enough for everyone to use, when our country was being settled. How we made soap in America in those early days is a story for another evening."

2. Setting Back the Clock

It was the following evening, after supper. The Martin family had settled down to read in the big chairs in the living room, and everyone was feeling very comfortable. They might have become sleepy, if father had not interrupted the quiet by saying, " Jimmy, please bring me the little clock from the desk."

Jimmy brought it, wondering what in the world clocks had to do with soap, which father had promised to talk about.

" Now," said father, " let's turn back the hands of this clock two hundred years."

Everybody's eyes popped open!

Everybody stared at father.

Father looked at them with a perfectly serious face.

" This is not a joke," said father. " Time is going to turn back to-night. Sue, put out the lights. We are going to imagine we are going back to two hundred years ago. Think of what living would be like in this country then. As soon as you have put yourselves back, tell me what you see."

Mother was quickest at the game of make-believe.

"I'm back there," said she. "We are living in a little log cabin. Outside of the cabin is a clearing of land, and the forest is close by."

"Yes, sirree," said Jimmy. "I can see that, and there are Indians in the forest."

"Then I'll stay in the clearing!" said Sue.

"Scare cat," said Jimmy. "I'm going into the forest."

"I am looking around our room," went on mother. "Our table is a long board, and our chairs are wooden benches."

"There is a candle on the table," said Sue.

"You helped me make that candle, Sue," said mother. "We hung a piece of string

down in a tin mold, and poured melted tallow fat around it, or we dipped the strings in melted tallow. When the fat hardened around the string, we had a candle."

"There is a fire in a big open fireplace," said father. "Jimmy and I cut the wood for it. Mother cooked our supper of corn-meal mush in an iron pot over the fire."

"I shall be spinning the yarn for your stockings and other clothes by the light of the fire this evening," added mother.

"By the way, Jimmy," mother went on, "to-morrow I intend to make soap. I do this twice a year, you know. I shall make it out of doors, and you must get a big pile of wood ready, and keep up the fire under the soap kettle."

"All right," said Jimmy. "That's a job I like."

"Have you saved enough fat for the soap?" asked father.

"Yes," said mother, "I've been saving all the fat we could spare all winter, and I have about thirty pounds."

"That should be enough for a barrel of soft soap," said father.

"I hope you have made plenty of lye, father," said mother.

"Lye?" said Sue. "What is lye?"

"Haven't you watched me pouring water

through that big barrel of wood ashes out in the yard?" asked father. "You have seen the liquid that trickles through the holes in the bottom of the barrel into the tub the barrel stands in. The water as it comes through dissolves something in the ashes that we call *potash.* The potash is in the solution that trickles through. This solution was put into a big iron pot, and lime was added. The lime changed the solution of potash to a stronger kind of potash that we call *lye*, or *potash lye.* This solution is so strong that it may take the skin from your fingers if you are not careful to keep them out of it. For that reason, because it is so burning on the skin, we often call it *caustic* potash. Does anyone here know what caustic means?"

"We can make a pretty good guess at it, father," said Jimmy.

"Why do you need the lye?" asked Sue.

"We could hardly make soap without lye of some kind, little daughter. Fat alone is not at all like soap, is it? But when fat and lye are mixed, they go together or combine, to make a new substance, which is soap. When this soap substance is put into water, it makes the water spread more easily than it did before.

"You know how easy it is to rub your hands together when you have soap suds on them. You know too that you cannot rub your hands together so easily if you use water without soap. Because water with soap in it spreads easily, it gets quickly around particles of dirt and grease and separates them from your hands.

"There's more to the cleaning story than this, of course; but we'll save the longer story for another night. Let me see, we were just putting fat and lye into the kettle, weren't we?"

"So that is why I boil the fat and lye together in the big kettle," said mother, "to make them combine as soap."

"I remember," said Jimmy, "that the Romans made soap of goat's tallow and wood ashes. So they must have known something about potash lye."

"Right!" said father. "And now," he went on, "since we are playing make-believe, we can imagine it is early to-morrow morning, and everything is ready to make soap. I have put a stout pole across two notched posts, and have hung the big iron kettle on it. Jimmy has made the fire under it, and mother has put in the fat and lye. Now you may take turns stirring with this long stick, while the fat and lye boil together."

"This kettle of soap is done," said mother after a while. "It is smooth and thick, like thick cream. Please empty it into a barrel, father, and we will start another kettleful."

"When I wash your clothes," went on mother, "I shall dip out some soap from the barrel with a dipper and put it into the water. This soap will stay soft, like a jelly."

"How could we make hard soap?" asked Jimmy.

"We should have to use caustic soda instead of caustic potash to make hard soap," said father, "and we haven't any way, here in the wilderness, of getting the soda."

"Shall we wash our hands with this soft soap?" said Sue.

"Not if you will go down to the beach and pick some of the bayberries that grow there," answered mother. "We will boil the bayberries in water until a fat comes out. Then, when the water cools, the fat can be skimmed off and boiled with lye to make a good soap for the hands. The bayberry fat makes pretty candles, too, which smell sweet and spicy as they burn."

Suddenly father switched on the electric lights. They all looked a little dazed. They had played their make-believe so hard, it almost seemed real to them, and they couldn't come back quickly to electric lights and steam radiators!

"Well," said mother, "that was hard work. I'm thankful that I don't really have to make the soap for the family in that way."

"And I," said father, "am glad that I don't have to save wood ashes and make lye."

"But I'm not so glad," said Jimmy. "I was having a dandy time keeping up the fire and watching out for Indians!"

— Ellen Beers McGowan (*Adapted*).

Which Is Right?

I

Write on a paper the numbers from 1 to 10. Choose the best words to finish each sentence and write them on your paper after the number of the sentence.

1. Instead of soap, people used to use

   flour and sugar.
   oil and sand.
   butter and eggs.

2. People used to wash clothes, without soap, in

   pails or tubs.
   kettles or pans.
   streams or pools.

3. The first people we know about who used soap were

   the Chinese and Japanese.
   the English and Spanish.
   the Gauls and Romans.

4. When the ashes were dug away from the city of Pompeii, the workers found

   a soap factory.
   a drug store.
   a moving-picture theatre.

5. When America was settled, people were just learning how

to use electric lights.
to make good soap.
to make good soup.

II

6. Soft soap is made from

fine white sand.
soda and ashes.
fats and potash lye.

7. Hard soap is made from

fats and caustic soda.
tallow and lye.
olive oil and lemons.

8. To make soft soap it is necessary that the fat and lye

should be dried.
should be baked.
should be boiled.

9. The early settlers in America used

washing powder.
soft soap.
hard soap.

10. The lye that the early settlers used in soft soap was made by letting water run

through corn meal.
through maple bark.
through wood ashes.

THINGS TO DO

1. Look at Jimmy's list of questions on pages 166–67. Which questions were not answered in the story? Try to answer these. You can find the answers and many more things about soap in a book by Ellen B. McGowan named *Soap Bubbles*. You can also read about soap in any encyclopedia that tells about common things.

2. If you live near a place where bayberries grow, it would be interesting to try to make some bayberry candles or bayberry soap. Your teacher or some other older person should help you with this.

3. Arrange these words in one alphabetic list. Then write after each word the definition you find in the "Short Dictionary" on pages 396–408:

royal	obelisk	caustic
dike	eruption	combine
crocodile	solution	tallow
volcano	lime	clearing

V
FOLK TALES

CHRISTMAS SNOW

Now the old Goose Mother
  Living in the sky
Shakes and shakes her feather beds
  Till the feathers fly.

Looking from her windows
  Maybe she can see,
Far below, the children
  Bringing home their tree.

Maybe she can hear them
  Shouting far below,
While they drag their Christmas tree
  Through the flying snow.

Old Mother — Goose Mother —
  Living far away,
Shaking out her feather beds
  Through the wintry day.

— KATHARINE PYLE.

SINTERKLAAS AND PIETERBAAS

Some stories that we read or hear told are new. Some stories are so old that our fathers, and grandfathers, and great-grandfathers and people even before that knew them. They are so old that no one knows who told them first. Such stories are called *folk tales.*

The idea in the poem " Christmas Snow " on page 187 came from a German folk tale. The story of " Sinterklaas and Pieterbaas " is a folk tale that is told in Holland.

1. Out of Spain into Holland

Once upon a time, very, very, very long ago, we are told, there lived in Spain a good old Bishop called Saint Nicholas. He lives there yet, folk in Holland say, with his servant Black Piet.

Every year Black Piet saddles a beautiful white horse and leads it to St. Nicholas's palace. The good old Saint mounts the horse and Black Piet jumps on a donkey. Off they go, Saint Nicholas and Black Piet, pacing softly and gently through towns and villages and over snow-clad mountains, till they come to a seaport and a great ship — Saint Nicholas's own ship, of course!

You should see that ship! It is crammed and jammed with the most wonderful gifts — with jumping-jacks, balls, dolls, picture-books, trains of cars, bags of sweet cakes and colored candies, and all sorts and kinds of beautiful things. Saint Nicholas steps aboard; so does Black Piet leading the white horse and the donkey.

Hi ho! Up goes the anchor, the sails are spread wide, and away speeds the good ship over the foaming waves to Holland.

You may be sure that every boy and girl in Holland is wild with delight as the Sixth of

December, Saint Nicholas Day, draws nearer and nearer. They are sure that this dear old Saint, who loves the Dutch children, is coming with a cargo of wonderful toys and goodies to give away on Saint Nicholas Day. He does not wait for our Christmas Day, you see.

And he does not give those fine toys and those delicious sweets to all the children. Oh no! Saint Nicholas and Black Piet, too, know just what each child has done during the year. If a child has been good, he will get nice presents. If he has been bad, he will get a switch. Some of the boys are scared, you may be sure, and some of the girls, too.

What jumping and joy there is all over Holland on the eve of Saint Nicholas Day. After the lights are lighted, the children wait eagerly, for it is Strewing Night. First comes a rap at the door — knock-knock-knock. Then Saint Nicholas enters, his eyes beaming with kindness and peace. On his head is his tall mitre, and his flowing robes glitter and shine with

gold and bright stones. The children dance about and sing, while the good Saint strews the most delicious candies about the room. While the children are merrily scrambling for them, he disappears.

Then the children set out their shoes and run away to bed. Oh, how excited they are! What will Sinterklaas and Pieterbaas leave in the shoes? For Sinterklaas and Pieterbaas, you must know, are the names the Dutch children call Saint Nicholas and Black Piet.

Now while the children are asleep all snug in their beds, who is that riding gently and softly over the house-tops? That is Sinterklaas, Saint Nicholas, riding on his white horse across the roofs. Pieterbaas is with him, and they have a great stack of toys and goodies to send down the chimneys.

In the morning how the children — the good ones of course — leap about with joy to find each shoe full of gifts, with a pile of other presents and goodies lying beside it. It is all very jolly on Saint Nicholas Day in the morning!

After that, Sinterklaas and Pieterbaas, with the white horse and the donkey, go back to Spain to stay till the next December.

2. Out of Holland into America

Long, long ago, three hundred years or more, when America was wild and Indians lived in the forests, some Dutch children came to America to live. They came with their fathers and mothers and brothers and sisters; and the place where they lived so long ago is now called New York. Of course, every year in December, Sinterklaas had to come out of Holland into America, to visit these children and bring them presents.

Then to America out of England came some English children to live in the wild new land. They, too, came with their fathers and mothers and brothers and sisters. They had never heard of Sinterklaas. At Christmas time in England, it was Old Father Christmas, with his jolly fat body, cherry-red nose, and flowing beard, who had brought them good things to eat and made Christmas gay. So it was Old Father Christmas whom the English children loved.

Now see what happened in America. The Dutch children's children and their children, and so on, became Americans. The English children's children and their children, and so on, became Americans. Sinterklaas, when in America, became American. He is Santa Claus!

You know what happens now. On the night before Christmas, you hang up your stocking. Santa Claus waits for that time.

While you are asleep — so our story goes — he comes riding over the house-tops in a sleigh full of toys, looking just like the English Father Christmas, round and jolly, with a cherry-colored nose, and a long beard.

And where is Pieterbaas? Why, Santa Claus must have left him behind in Holland, where he left his bishop's robe and mitre.

— FRANCES JENKINS OLCOTT (*Adapted*).

FIND THE RIGHT ENDING

Copy the numbers and each of the ten names. Look at the sentence endings that follow the names. Write after each name the sentence ending that goes with that name.

1. Black Piet
2. Father Christmas
3. Holland
4. New York
5. Pieterbaas
6. Spain
7. Sinterklaas
8. Santa Claus
9. Saint Nicholas
10. Saint Nicholas Day

—— is the name the Dutch children call Saint Nicholas.

—— is the name the Dutch children call Black Piet.
——, the story says, lives in a palace in Spain.
—— is the country that Sinterklaas visits.
—— makes Christmas gay for English children.
—— is the place in America that was settled by the Dutch.
—— got his name from Sinterklaas.
—— is the Dutch Christmas.
——, the story says, is the servant of Saint Nicholas.
——, the story says, is the country where Saint Nicholas lives.

Things to Do

1. The story "Sinterklaas and Pieterbaas" is taken from a book named *Wonder Tales from Windmill Lands.* It is by Frances Jenkins Olcott. Perhaps you will like to read some of the other stories. Can you tell why Holland is called a "Windmill Land"?

2. The story "Sinterklaas and Pieterbaas" is in two parts. See if you can think of other names for the two parts that would do as well as those given in the book.

3. Try to find a good story, or poem, or picture about Christmas and bring it for the class to read or see.

THREE MEALS SHORTEN THE DAY

This is another folk tale from Holland. It comes from Edam Town, where they make fine yellow cheeses.

Once upon a time a stout lad named Hans, with a scythe on his back, came into the land near Edam Town. How he stared all about him! The meadows were so fresh and green, and the cows were so big and well-kept, it was good to see. The farmers, with long pipes in their mouths, were strolling about the fields.

Hans shook his head, and felt of his empty stomach.

"Here is where one can earn something," he thought.

He stepped up to a certain Farmer, who was standing in his doorway, and said,

" My name is Hans. I should like to work for you. How much wages do you pay here? "

" Is your work good, Hans? " asked the Farmer.

" Is my work good! That I will leave to you to see! " said Hans.

" Well, you may go to work at once," said the Farmer.

The hot porridge was standing on the breakfast table, and Hans looked toward it with longing eyes. Oh, how it steamed and how good it smelled!

"Do I get something to eat, good Farmer, if I work?"

The Farmer laughed. "Of course, Hans, of course."

"How many meals a day?"

"Three meals, Hans — breakfast, dinner at noon, and supper."

"May I ask if you give breakfast *now?*"

"Yes, Hans. Sit down and begin. Eat all you want."

"This is a good land!" thought Hans. "Here I can always get a meal."

A bowl filled with hot porridge was set before him. With spoon, with fist, and with smacking lips he ate it all. Then he shut his eyes and nodded with delight.

"Now to work, Hans," smiled the good-natured Farmer.

"Well said!" answered Hans, and he got up from his chair.

At the door he stood looking like a trusting puppy that had never been beaten.

"Good Farmer," he said, "will you let me ask one little thing more?"

"Go ahead, Hans. Say what is on your mind. But make it short and sweet, for there is much work to do."

"This is what I thought," said Hans. "Why must I wait for dinner? Why not have dinner now?"

"Dinner, Hans! Why it is early in the morning!" cried the Farmer.

The Farmer's Wife stood near, and she gave her husband a poke in the ribs and beckoned him into a corner. She laid her fingers on her lips, and whispered: "If he eats dinner now, he will not have to eat it at twelve o'clock. Then if he does not have to come all the way to the house, we shall save much time. Do you not understand that, you donkey?"

" Are you sure about that? " asked the Farmer wonderingly. Then turning to Hans, he said, " Sit down. My wife will give you your dinner now."

The Farmer's Wife had the potatoes already peeled, and she set them on the fire. When they were done she added a piece of butter as big as her fist and some solid chunks of meat. Hans, even in his dreams, had never seen anything like that. He rubbed his eyes and fell to eating.

He clawed and he gnawed, for Hans knew little of table manners. Dinner went quicker than breakfast, though he had eaten a big bowl of porridge. At last he wiped his mouth with the flat of his hand and, looking at the empty bowl, he sighed. Not a crumb of potato, not a drop of gravy, not a tiny morsel of meat was left there.

With slow steps he went to the door. There he turned again slowly like some one saying farewell to his country.

" Have you had enough, Hans? " laughed the Farmer.

" Good Farmer," said Hans in his honest voice, " have you not spoken of supper? "

" Why, yes, I did mention it," answered the Farmer. " We eat supper here in the evening. How is it at your house? "

Hans scratched his ear. Just then the Farmer's Wife came again to the rescue. She drew the Farmer into the corner, and playfully poked him in the ribs.

" Let him have his supper now," she whispered. " It is a long way from the field to the house. If he has had his supper, we shall save still more time."

Then she began to cut many slices of bread, and to spread the slices with plenty of sweet-smelling butter. Hans watched her as a child watches some one about to give him a treat; and when she cut a big lump of rich golden-yellow Edam cheese, the eyes of the poor fellow fairly watered with happiness. Oh! if his

father and mother could have seen him then, it would have been the most joyful moment of his life.

He sat down like a prince at the table and filled his cheeks full, hardly taking time to chew. In no time the mountain of bread and butter and Edam cheese was gone. The Farmer watched from the doorway.

"Are you done, Hans?" he asked patiently.

"I am coming! I am coming!" answered Hans.

As soon as they went out of doors, Hans began to look around and to draw in breaths of the fresh morning air.

"Now you must feel like doing a good day's work, Hans," said the Farmer, "since you have eaten so heartily."

"Work?" said Hans in surprise. "Work, good Farmer? Do you expect me to work?"

"Yes, of course; the day is only begun."

"But I have just eaten supper," said Hans. "At home, we sleep after supper."

And no matter what the Farmer said or did, as soon as they came to the first haycock, Hans threw himself down. In a twinkling he was snoring away so loud that you could not hear the songs of the larks.

The Farmer scolded and shouted and whacked him with his fists. It was of no use. Hans slept sweetly on, caring nothing for the troubles and pains of this life. For Hans the Hungry had had his supper!

— FRANCES JENKINS OLCOTT (*Adapted*).

Why Do You Think So?

Tell or write the answers to these four questions. With each answer give the reason why you think as you do.

1. Was Hans dishonest or merely silly?

2. Was the Farmer's Wife dishonest or silly or both?

3. Would Hans have been likely to do good work that day, if he had been willing to work?

4. Was Hans likely to get many more meals in Edam Town?

Things to Do

1. This story is taken from *Wonder Tales from Windmill Lands* by Frances Jenkins Olcott. What other story have you read from the same book? If you like to read about Holland, you will enjoy *The Dutch Twins*, by Lucy F. Perkins, and *Child Life in Other Lands*, by H. Avis Perdue.

2. "Three Meals Shorten the Day" would make a very funny little play for a small group of children to give for the rest of the class or to another group. It would be good in a mixed program when some children give one part of the entertainment and others give other parts.

3. Write on a paper the numbers from 1 to 20. In each line — not column — below, there is one word that is opposite in meaning from the first word in the line. Pick out each of these and write it after the number of its line. For example, the opposite of *came* is *went;* so you will write, *1. went.*

1.	came	ran	walked	went
2.	delight	sorrow	joy	fun
3.	solid	dark	queer	liquid
4.	powerful	sweet	weak	brave
5.	forget	remember	report	tell
6.	greatest	least	finest	kindest
7.	finished	helped	found	began
8.	shorten	lengthen	pull	brush
9.	now	here	there	then
10.	freezing	trying	melting	lifting
11.	delicious	good	tender	unpleasant
12.	plenty	few	dangerous	several
13.	end	beginning	corner	center
14.	improve	earn	creep	injure
15.	wonderful	polite	ordinary	magical
16.	beautiful	hard	ugly	yellow
17.	loud	queer	unkind	soft
18.	coming	going	hopping	waiting
19.	cold	hollow	white	warm
20.	awake	ready	asleep	prepared

THE GOLDEN TOUCH

This folk tale comes to us from Greece. It is very, very old.

1. Midas and His Treasure

Once upon a time there lived a king whose name was Midas. He had one child, a little daughter whose name was Marygold.

This King Midas was fonder of gold than of anything else in the world. If he loved anything better, or as much, it was his merry little daughter. But the more Midas loved his daughter, the more did he wish for wealth.

He thought that the best thing he could possibly do for Marygold would be to leave her a great pile of yellow, glistening coin. He wanted to gather more gold than anyone else had ever had. He gave all his thoughts and all his time to this one purpose.

If he happened to look at the gold-tinted clouds at sunset, he wished that they were real gold and that he could put them into his strong box. When little Marygold ran to meet him with a bunch of buttercups, he would say, " If those flowers were as golden as they look, they would be worth picking."

When he was younger and before he had become so eager for riches, King Midas had been very fond of flowers. He had planted a large rose garden. In that garden he had raised the biggest, sweetest, and most beautiful roses to be seen in that country. The roses still bloomed in the garden, but King Midas no longer cared about them. Sometimes he looked at them, however, and wished that each rose-petal was a thin plate of gold. Midas had once been fond of music, too. But now the only music he cared for was the clink of one coin against another.

People always grow more and more foolish unless they take pains to grow wiser and wiser. After a time, Midas could hardly bear to see or touch anything that was not made of gold. He spent a large part of every day in a dreary underground room in his palace, counting his treasure.

When he went into his treasure room, he always locked the door. Then he would take a bag of gold coin, or a great gold bowl, or a peck measure of gold-dust and carry it to one corner of the room. In this corner, a little sun came in through a barred window.

Midas would look at the sun shining on his treasure and say to himself, "O Midas, rich King Midas, what a happy man you are!" Sometimes his own face seemed to be laughing at him from the polished side of a cup or bowl. It was almost as though some one were making fun of him, but Midas did not notice this.

2. The Wish

One day when Midas was in his treasure room, a shadow fell on the heaps of gold. He looked up and saw a young man standing in the sunbeam. The stranger had a bright cheerful face, and his smile seemed to lighten the dark room.

Midas knew that he had locked the door. He did not see how the stranger could have entered. He was not frightened, however, for the young man looked kind and as though he meant no harm.

"You are a wealthy man, King Midas," said the visitor. "I doubt if any other room in the world holds as much gold as you have here."

"I have done pretty well — pretty well," said Midas, in a discontented voice. "But after all, this isn't much. Think how many

years it took me to get it together. If I could live a thousand years, I might have time to grow rich."

"What!" cried the stranger. "Then you are not satisfied!"

Midas shook his head.

"Tell me what would satisfy you," said the stranger. "I should be glad to know."

Midas thought very carefully before he answered. In his mind he was piling one golden mountain upon another. At last he had a bright idea. Raising his head, he looked the stranger in the face.

"Well, Midas," said his visitor, "I see you have thought of something that will satisfy you. Tell me your wish."

"It is this," said Midas. "I am tired of collecting my treasures so slowly. I wish everything that I touch could be changed to gold."

The stranger's smile grew so broad that it seemed to light the room like sunshine.

"The Golden Touch!" he exclaimed. "Are you quite sure that will satisfy you, friend Midas?"

"How could it fail to satisfy me?" said Midas.

"Are you sure you will never be sorry that you have it?"

"How could I be sorry?" asked Midas. "That is all I need to make me perfectly happy."

"It shall be as you wish, then," replied the stranger. "Tomorrow, at sunrise, you will have the Golden Touch."

The figure of the young man suddenly became so bright that Midas closed his eyes. When he opened them, his visitor had disappeared.

3. The Golden Touch

The story does not say whether Midas slept as usual that night. He probably felt like a child to whom a beautiful new plaything has been promised in the morning.

At any rate, day had hardly peeped over the hills, when King Midas was broad awake. At once he stretched out his arms and began to touch the objects that were nearest him. Nothing happened. Everything was just as it had been. Midas was bitterly disappointed.

Just then a bright ray of sunshine came through the window. As it shone on his bed, it seemed to Midas that the covering of the bed looked yellow instead of white. Looking more carefully, he saw that the linen had turned into a fine, woven cloth of gold.

Midas jumped up, filled with joy, and dashed about the room. He took hold of a bed post and it became a golden one. He picked up a book. It turned to gold with thin golden plates for leaves. It could no longer be read, but Midas did not stop to worry about that.

He put on his clothes and found that he was wearing gold cloth. He picked up a handkerchief. This became gold, too. The King was a little sorry when this change happened. Marygold had hemmed the handkerchief for him and he would have liked to keep it as it was. Then too, cloth of gold is not very soft on one's nose.

Midas next picked up his spectacles and put them on. They turned to gold at once, so of course he could not see through them. "Well," said the King, "I shall have to get along without spectacles. But I can see well enough for most purposes, and Marygold will soon be able to read to me."

It was not yet time for his breakfast, so Midas went into the garden. Here he walked about among the rosebushes. As he walked, he touched each flower and bud. The roses, which had been full of color and scent, were changed at once. They became gold and all their perfume disappeared. Much pleased, King Midas went in to eat his breakfast.

On this particular morning, his cook had prepared a breakfast that looked very good to the King. I am not sure what a king ate in those days, but I think Midas had some nice little brook trout, baked potatoes, hot wheat cakes, fresh boiled eggs, and coffee. Marygold probably had an orange, oatmeal and cream, and a glass of milk.

King Midas asked that Marygold be called. He waited to begin his breakfast till she should come. It was not a great while before he heard her coming, crying bitterly. This surprised him, for Marygold was one of the most cheerful little people you would see in a summer's day. She hardly shed a thimbleful of tears in a year's time.

She was still crying loudly when she came into the room.

"How now, little lady!" cried Midas. "What is the matter with you this bright morning?"

Marygold held out her hand. In it was one of the golden roses from the garden.

"Beautiful!" said her father. "What is there about this splendid golden rose to make you cry?"

"Oh, Father dear," answered the child, "it is not beautiful. It is the ugliest flower that ever grew. As soon as I was dressed I ran to the garden to pick some roses for you. But — oh dear! — what do you think had happened? All the beautiful roses that looked so lovely and smelled so sweet are spoiled. They have grown hard and yellow and they have no sweet smell. What can be the matter with them?"

"Now, my dear little girl," said Midas, "don't cry about it. You can easily exchange one of those golden roses for a great many of the kind that will wither in a day. Sit down and eat your breakfast."

"I don't like such roses as this," said Marygold, tossing the flower scornfully away. "It has no smell and the petals prick my nose."

The little girl sat down at the table and began, rather sadly, to eat her breakfast. Midas poured himself a cup of coffee, and the coffee pot at once turned to gold. He lifted a spoonful of coffee to his lips. As soon as it touched his mouth, the coffee turned to melted gold and in a moment became a hard lump.

"Ha!" exclaimed Midas, much startled.

"What is the matter, Father?" asked Marygold.

"Nothing, child, nothing," said Midas. "Eat your oatmeal before it gets cold."

He took one of the little trout on his plate. Then he touched it with his finger to see what would happen. At once it became a gold fish. It was not of course one of those pretty little fish that swim about in glass bowls filled with water. It was a solid gold trout.

Next the King tried a boiled egg, but it changed at his touch, just as the trout had done. It might very well have come from the goose we have all read about that laid the golden eggs.

"I don't quite see," thought King Midas to himself, "how I am going to get any breakfast."

He decided that he would try to eat something very quickly before it had a chance to change to gold. So he snatched a small hot potato and tried to cram it into his mouth and swallow it.

In a moment he found his mouth full, not of hot potato, but of solid metal. It burned his tongue so badly that he jumped up from

the table. In pain and fright, he danced and stamped about the room.

"Father, dear Father!" cried little Marygold. "What is the matter? Have you burned your mouth?"

"Ah, dear child!" groaned Midas. "I don't know what is to become of your poor father."

Marygold gazed at him in distress. Then as he groaned again, she ran to him and threw her arms about him.

Midas bent down and kissed her.

"My precious, precious Marygold!" cried he.

But Marygold made no answer.

What had the King done! How fatal was the stranger's gift! The moment the lips of Midas touched Marygold's face, a change had taken place.

Her sweet rosy face became yellow and shining. Her beautiful brown curls took the same tint. Her little body grew hard within her father's arms. Marygold was a human child no longer. She was a little golden statue.

It would be too sad a story if I were to tell how Midas wrung his hands and groaned. He could neither bear to look at Marygold nor to look away from her.

Gold was no longer beautiful to him. He would have been glad to be the poorest man in the kingdom if this would have brought back the rose-color to his dear child's face.

4. Another Wish

In the midst of his distress, Midas saw a stranger standing at the door. He knew at once who the visitor was. It was the young man who the day before had given him the gift of the Golden Touch.

"Well, friend Midas," said the stranger, "how do you succeed with the Golden Touch?"

Midas shook his head.

"I am very unhappy," said he.

"Very unhappy!" said the stranger. "How is that? Have I not kept my promise? Did I not give you what you wanted most?"

"Gold is not everything," said Midas. "I have lost all that my heart really cared for."

"Ah! you have made a discovery since yesterday," said the stranger. "Let us see, then. Which of these things do you think is worth the more, the Golden Touch or one cup of clear, cool water?"

"Oh, clear, cool water!" said Midas. "It will never moisten my dry throat again."

"The Golden Touch," went on the stranger, "or a crust of bread."

"A piece of bread is better than gold," said Midas sadly.

"The Golden Touch," said the stranger, "or your own little Marygold, warm and loving, as she was an hour ago?"

"Oh, my child, my dear child!" cried poor Midas, wringing his hands. "I would not have given the dimple in her chin for the power of turning the whole earth into gold."

"You are wiser than you were, King Midas," said the stranger. "I was afraid that your own heart had hardened into gold. I can see now that it has not. Do you really want to give up the Golden Touch?"

"It is hateful to me," replied Midas.

As he spoke, a fly settled on his nose. It

turned to gold at once and fell to the floor.

"Go," said the stranger, "and plunge into the little river that flows past the foot of your garden. Take a pitcher of the same water and sprinkle it on anything that you want to change from gold to what it was before. In this way you may be able to correct the harm you have done."

King Midas bowed low. When he lifted his head, the stranger had vanished.

Midas lost no time in snatching a big pitcher. It was earthenware, but it turned to gold when he picked it up. He dashed off to the riverside. It was wonderful to see the bushes and other plants turn yellow as he hurried through them. When he reached the river, he plunged in. He did not even stop to take off his shoes.

"Poof! poof! poof!" snorted King Midas as his head came out of the water. "I think that must have washed away the Golden Touch. Now I'll fill my pitcher."

As he dipped the pitcher into the water, it turned from gold to earthenware. How happy the King was to see this change!

He hurried back to the palace. The servants must have been surprised to see the King carrying a big pitcher of water. They did not know how precious that water was to him. The first thing he did was to sprinkle handfuls of it over the little golden Marygold.

As soon as the water fell on her, the rosy color came back to her face. She began to sneeze and sputter. She was surprised to find her father throwing water on her.

"Don't do that, dear Father," she cried. "See how you have wet my nice clean frock."

For Marygold did not know she had been a little golden statue. She did not remember anything except that she had run to her father when he burned his mouth.

King Midas did not tell his daughter how foolish he had been. Instead he took her into the garden to see the roses. He sprinkled water on the golden ones and they became sweet again. Then they both went indoors and the King had a real breakfast.

Midas was a much wiser king from that time. He tried to do good with his gold instead of saving it.

As long as he lived, two things reminded him of the Golden Touch. One was that the sands of the little river sparkled like gold. The other was that Marygold's hair had a golden look that it had not had before. It was really prettier than it had been. When she grew up and had children, their hair was golden too. When he was an old man, King Midas used often to look at the pretty heads of his grandchildren and say, "That is the best gold of all."

— Nathaniel Hawthorne (*Adapted*).

An Outline to Complete

Copy this outline and fill in the parts that are left out. You do not need to use the exact words of the book, but what you write must agree with the story.

You may look up in the story anything you have forgotten. Do not write anything in your book.

The Golden Touch

I. Midas and His Treasure

1. Midas was a . . . . .
2. He had a daughter . . . . .
3. Midas loved gold more than . . . . .
4. He spent a great deal of time . . . . .
5. He kept his wealth in . . . . .

II. The Wish

1. One day Midas was . . . . .
2. There appeared, in the dark room, . . .
3. Midas and the visitor . . . . .
4. The stranger promised that Midas should have . . . . .

III. The Golden Touch

1. The next day, when Midas awoke, the sun . . . . .
2. As soon as the sun rose, everything that Midas touched . . . . .
3. Midas did not like it when his breakfast .
4. Marygold ran to her father to . . . . .
5. When Midas touched Marygold, she . . . .
6. At once, the king felt . . . . .

IV. Another Wish

1. As he mourned, Midas looked up and saw . . . .
2. The stranger asked Midas if he wanted to give up . . . .
3. Midas said that the Golden Touch was . .
4. The stranger told Midas what to do to . .
5. Midas was able to change things from their golden form by . . . .
6. After that Midas never . . . .

Things to Do

1. "The Golden Touch" is taken from *The Wonder Book*, by Nathaniel Hawthorne. If you read *The Wonder Book* and like it, you will also like *Tanglewood Tales* by the same author. If you find them a little hard, ask some one to read them to you.

2. "The Golden Touch" would make a good play. If you play it, how many acts will you have? Can you use more people than Midas, Marygold, and the stranger? How can you let the audience know, in an interesting way, how fond Midas was of gold? Can you use extra people to help about this? What other people may have been in the dining room when the king and his daughter were at breakfast?

VI

MAKE-BELIEVE

A·G·DUCK

THE OLD BRASS POT *

The old brass pot in the corner
Shines and scowls at the kitchen pans;
Like a stubborn king
He sits and frowns. . . .
Orders them about
When I'm not looking.
He was a gift from a fairy queen. . . .
What can I do?

He boils rice when I want it,
Makes broth when it is needed;
He is magic,
But he growls all day.
Without him it would be pleasant and
comfortable
In my little cottage

* Reprinted by permission from *Shoes of the Wind* by Hilda Conkling. Copyright, 1922, by Frederick A. Stokes Company.

With wistaria growing over the open windows;
What can I do?

He tells the frying-pan
To stay on its hook . . .
He shouts at the other pans
In a gruff voice;
They all might be happy
In my cozy kitchen!
Tell me . . . but you must whisper . . .
What can I do?

— HILDA CONKLING.

THINGS TO DO

1. This poem is from *Shoes of the Wind.* The author was a little girl when she wrote the book. Other books of poems, that you may like to read, are *Silver Pennies* by Blanche Jennings Thompson and *Magpie Lane* by Nancy Byrd Turner.

2. If you would enjoy doing it, try writing a poem yourself. It may be about something real like the poem about a rabbit on page 63, or about something fanciful like the poem you have just read.

THE GOLDEN GOOSE

This story is an English folk tale told in the form of a play. Plays that you see in the theater are written like this one. First comes the title, then a list of all the people in the play, then the play itself. The name of each person who speaks comes just before the words he says. Words that are not speeches, but that tell what is on the stage or how people are to move about, are in italics.

People of the Play

JACK	THE KING
HIS MOTHER	THE QUEEN
THE OLD MAN	THE PRINCESS
THE LANDLORD	THE DOCTOR
HIS DAUGHTER	THE HERALD
HIS WIFE	COUNT NIMBLEWIT
THE SEXTON	PRINCE VIVIEN
THE CLERK	THE LADY-IN-WAITING

THE GUARD

Scene 1

A highway with trees at the back. At the left there is the door of the inn. A table with two stools stands near the door.

As the play begins, Jack and his Mother enter at the right. She carries Jack's dinner in a basket. He carries an ax over his shoulder. Jack is a gay, care-free lad. His mother looks worried and cross.

Jack: Well, Mother, I hope you have plenty of good food there for my dinner, for I am as hungry as a bear.

Mother: Plenty for a simple lad who wastes his time and does not earn enough to buy his food.

Jack: Oho! Perhaps I am not so simple as you think. I may make a fortune and marry the King's daughter yet. Who knows?

Mother: Ha! Ha! Ha! The King's daughter marry a lazy good-for-nothing like you! That's very likely to happen!

Jack: Well now, maybe I'll find the pot of gold at the rainbow's end and be a rich man some day.

[*He stops in the middle of the stage and puts down his ax.*]

Mother: Gold, indeed! If you ever have as much as a dozen copper pennies, that's all I ask. Here, take the basket. I must go home.

[*She gives him the basket and starts to go.*]

Jack: Cheer up, Mother; I may surprise you yet!

Mother: Do a good day's work and come home to-night with honest wages in your pocket. That will be surprise enough for me!

[*She goes out. Jack scratches his head and looks around.*]

Jack: It is a long time since breakfast, but a longer time to dinner. Woodcutting is hard work. I think I'll just take a bite before I begin.

[*He sits down on the ground and opens the basket.*]

Bread and cheese and a bottle of milk. Aha! Poor Jack is going to have a good dinner.

[*An old ragged man with a staff enters at the right.*]

Old Man: Good day to you, lad! Won't you give a poor old man a mouthful?

Jack: Well now, it's not much that I have

to eat, but what there is I'll share. Take some of this.

[*He hands the bread and cheese to the old man.*]

Old Man: Ah! That tastes good!

[*He gobbles it all down.*]

Jack: Hey there! Not so fast! Don't be greedy. What! Not a crumb left! Well, Jack, that leaves poor pickings for you.

[*He starts to take a drink.*]

Old Man: Won't you give an old man a sip?

Jack: Well now, it's not much that I have to drink, but what I have I'll share.

[*He gives the bottle to the Old Man, who drinks it all.*]

Hi there! Softly, softly! What! Not a drop left? Bread and cheese gone, milk gone. So poor Jack must go hungry and thirsty too!

Old Man: Now, my lad, don't be put out. You have done an old man a good turn, and don't think you shall lose by it. If you do

as I say, you shall always have whatever you please to eat and drink after this.

Jack: Eh? How's that?

Old Man: Only do
As I tell you:
Take three steps right
And three steps left,
Turn around twice,
Follow your nose;

In a trice
You will see
A hollow tree
And in the cleft
A goose of gold,
If you do
As you are told.

[*The Old Man goes out. Jack starts to follow the directions.*]

Jack: What did he say? Three steps right. Three steps left. Turn around twice. Follow your nose. Here, indeed, is a hollow tree; and, sure enough, in the cleft a goose of gold!

[*He picks up the goose and puts it under his arm.*]

Well now, I must be a rich man; and since I am a rich man I think I'll go to court and see the King. But first I'll get some dinner, the finest dinner that money can buy.

[*He crosses to the inn door and raps loudly on it.*]

Ho, Landlord! What! Landlord, I say!

[*The Landlord looks out of the door.*]

Landlord: What do you want, you shabby rascal?

Jack: Bring out the best you have to eat and drink.

Landlord: Why, Master Rags, you couldn't pay for a penny loaf, I'm sure. Not a crumb shall you have unless you pay me first.

Jack: Here, take this.

[*He gives the Landlord a feather from the goose, then seats himself at the table.*]

Landlord: What! This is a feather of pure gold! Why, sir, you must be King Midas himself! Here, Wife! Daughter! Bring roast meat. Bring fine white bread. Bring the best in the house!

[*His Wife and Daughter hurry out carrying dishes, which they place on the table before Jack, who starts to eat at once.*]

Does the meat suit your worship?

Jack: Why, it's good enough.

Landlord: Is the bread to your worship's taste?

Jack: I've eaten worse.

Landlord: I'll go and bring a new loaf for your worship.

[*He hurries out. His Wife and Daughter stay. They watch Jack and talk softly together.*]

Wife: Did you ever see the like? A goose of pure gold!

Daughter: Oh, Mother, if I had only just one feather from its tail!

Wife: Hush! the young man is growing sleepy. Wait till he's asleep. Then you can take a feather and no one will ever know.

[*She goes out.*]

Daughter: Oh, sir, do you wish some more meat, sir?

[*Jack snores softly.*]

He's asleep! Now's my chance! It's going to be easy.

[*She starts to pull a feather from the goose's tail and then suddenly cries out.*]

Oh, oh, I'm stuck! I can't let go!

[*Jack wakes up.*]

Jack: Hey? What's this?

Daughter: Oh, sir, kind sir, I can't let go of your goose!

Jack: What! Trying to steal a feather, were you? Well then, it serves you right.

[*He stands up.*]

Daughter: Oh, sir, please let me go. The bread is in the oven and it will burn if I don't take it out.

Jack: I can't help that, I'm sure. Where I go, goose goes; and I'm going to see the King.

[*He starts to walk off just as the Wife enters.*]

Wife: Why! Why! You shameless girl! To run after a young man like that! Stop this instant!

Daughter: But I can't let go!

Wife: Well, I'll soon see that you do!

[*She takes hold of the girl.*]

Why, what's the matter? I'm stuck fast! Young man, how dare you! Stop, stop, I tell you!

Jack: Shan't, Ma'am. Can't, Ma'am. Where I go, goose goes; and I'm going to see the King.

[*The Landlord comes in.*]

Landlord: Wife! Wife! What's this?

Have you gone mad? Stop! Come back! Come back!

Wife: I can't let go!

Landlord: What! Well, I'll make you let go fast enough!

[*He catches hold of her arm.*]

Oh! Oh! Oh! Help, help! I'm stuck! Help!

Jack: It seems to me that I am going to have company.

Daughter: Kind sir, good sir, the bread is in the oven. Please let me go!

Wife: The meat is roasting on the spit. It will be spoiled. It will burn to a cinder. Please let me go!

Landlord: The wine is running from the tap. Oh, sir, let us go!

Jack: Shan't, sir. Can't, sir. Where I go, goose goes; and I'm off to see the King.

[*The Sexton comes in.*]

Sexton: Landlord! Landlord! Where are you going? Wait! Have you forgotten that you were to serve a christening feast this noon?

Landlord: I can't help that! I can't get away.

Sexton: But, my dear man, you mustn't go off like this. Think of the christening!

[*He catches hold of the Landlord's arm.*]

Why! Why! Why! What is this? I can't get loose! What sort of trick is this? Young man, if this is your doing, I beg of you to stop at once!

Jack: Shan't, sir. Can't, sir. Where I go, goose goes; and I'm off to see the King.

[*The Clerk comes in.*]

Clerk: What's this? What's this? What kind of game is this the Sexton is playing? Sir, this is not at all proper. I bid you stop at once.

[*He lays hold of the Sexton.*]

What! What! What! You naughty rogue, how dare you treat me like this? I'll have you hanged! I'll have the whole lot of you hanged unless you stop at once! Stop, I say!

Jack: Shan't, sir. Can't, sir. Where I go, goose goes; and I'm off to see the King.

[*All this time he has been tramping back and forth with the others following. Now he starts off towards the right.*]

Daughter: Let me go! Oh, please let me go!

Wife: Stop! Stop at once, I say!

Landlord: Help! Help! Help!

Sexton: Stop, I beg you, stop!

Clerk: I'll have you hanged, you young rascal!

Jack: Come now, friends, we must step along lively if we want to reach the palace before night. Now then, all together — left foot, right foot, left foot, right foot.

[*He leads them off right.*]

All: Help! Stop! Let me go! You shall be hanged! Stop! Stop! Let me go, you rascal.

Scene 2

In the King's Palace. The King, the Queen, and the Princess are seated on their thrones. The Lady-in-Waiting and the Guard stand one at each side. The Doctor stands beside the Princess, who is very pretty but looks mournful and wipes away tears with her handkerchief.

Doctor: And what is the nature of your daughter's illness?

Queen: Oh, sir, she does nothing but moan and sigh and sigh and moan from morning until night.

Doctor: Does she never laugh at all?

King: She has never been known to laugh since she was born.

Doctor: Ahem! Put out your tongue.

[*He looks at her tongue through a reading glass.*]

It is as I feared. She has the crying sickness, or, as it is sometimes called, the doldrums. Aside from that, she is perfectly well.

Princess: Give me another handkerchief!

[*The Lady-in-Waiting gives her a handkerchief. She starts to sniff loudly.*]

King: Cure her, Doctor, and you shall be a rich man.

Doctor: Alas! I cannot! My medicine is of no use here. There is just one cure for such a case. Some one must make the Princess laugh. If she once laughs hard, she will be cured.

King: But we have tried everything. Time and again I have put on my crown upside down and ordered all the courtiers to stand on their heads in rows, but it only made her cry the louder.

Doctor: You must try harder. The Princess must be made to laugh. That is all I have to say, Your Majesty.

[*The Doctor bows low and goes out.*]

Queen: What can we do?

King: There is just one way left.

[*He turns to the Guard*]

Summon the Herald.

Guard: It shall be done, Your Majesty.

[*He goes out.*]

Queen: You are going to try *that?* Oh dear!

[*The Guard comes back with the Herald.*]

King: Go, Sir Herald. Stand on the Palace steps and proclaim that whoever makes the Princess laugh shall be rewarded by the gift of her hand in marriage and one half the kingdom. But whoever tries and fails shall have a good drubbing.

Herald: Your Majesty shall be obeyed.

[*The Herald goes out.*]

Princess: Oh, boohoo! Boohoo! I'm so unhappy! Boohoo! Boohoo! Give me another handkerchief! This one is all w-w-wet!

Lady-in-Waiting: Here is another handkerchief, your Royal Highness.

Princess: Oh, boohoo! Boohoo!

[*The Herald enters.*]

Herald: Your Majesty, Count Nimblewit is here. He has come to make the Princess laugh.

King: Bid him come in.

[*Count Nimblewit enters. He bows low before the thrones. The Herald goes out.*]

Count Nimblewit: Your Highness, I am going to make you laugh. Only listen while I tell you a funny story. Once upon a time there was a donkey who wanted to be a dragon —

Princess: But I know that one.

Count Nimblewit: Then let me tell you the tale of the caterpillar who fell in love with a cabbage worm.

Princess: I've heard it before!

Count Nimblewit: Then let me tell you the story of the pigs and the three princesses.

Princess: But I know it by heart already! Oh, boohoo! Boohoo! Send him away! He m-m-makes me cry!

King: Sir, it is plain that you are wasting your breath.

[*to Guard*]

Take him away and see that he has a good drubbing.

[*The Guard takes out Count Nimblewit.*]

Princess: Oh, boohoo! Boohoo! Life is so sad! Give me another handkerchief!

[*The Herald enters.*]

Herald: Your Majesty, Prince Vivien is here. He is sure that he can make the Princess laugh.

King: Well, send him in.

[*Prince Vivien enters. He bows low before the thrones. The Herald goes out.*]

Prince Vivien: Your Highness, I can certainly make you laugh. Look at me. Did you ever see as funny a face as this?

[*He makes a funny face.*]

Princess: Oh! The poor man!

Prince Vivien: Or one like this?

[*He makes a worse face.*]

Princess: Oh! Oh! I think he must have a dreadful pain!

Prince Vivien: Or one like this?

[*He makes a still worse one.*]

Princess: Oh, boohoo! Boohoo! Send him away! He makes me so sad! Boohoo! Where is my handkerchief?

King: Sir, it is plain that you are merely wasting time.

[*to Guard*]

Take him away and see that he has a good drubbing.

[*The Guard takes out Prince Vivien.*]

Princess: Oh! I'm so unhappy!

Queen: This is too distressing. Nothing seems to do any good.

King: I'm afraid it is hopeless.

[*The Herald enters.*]

Heralds: Your Majesty, there is a simpleton outside who wishes to see Your Majesty.

King: Send him away. This is no time for nonsense.

Herald: Your Majesty, I think you would do well to see him. Indeed, he is a rare sight! Ha, ha!

King: How so?

Herald: He says he has brought a goose for Your Majesty, but in truth it's a whole flock of geese that follow him!

King: Then send him in. We will see these geese.

[*The Herald goes out.*]

Princess: Boohoo! Life is so sad, so sad!

[*Cries are heard outside. Jack enters followed by the Daughter, the Wife, the Landlord, the Sexton, and the Clerk.*]

Jack: Come now, all together! Left foot, right foot. Step right up to the throne and bow to the King and Queen.

Landlord: Help! Help! Help!

Daughter: Oh, I'm so tired!

Wife: Let me go! Let me go!

Sexton: Somebody stop him! Stop him at once!

Clerk: The rascal must be hanged!

All: Your Majesty, we appeal! We protest, Your Majesty!

Princess: Oh, ha, ha, ha! Hee, hee, hee! Just look at them! Did you ever see such a sight! Oh, what a joke! Ha, ha, ha! Ha, ha, ha! Ha, ha, ha!

[*The Princess fairly doubles up with laughter.*]

Queen: She laughed!

Lady-in-Waiting: The Princess laughed!

Guard: The Princess laughed!

King: She laughed! She's cured! She's cured!

Princess: Ha, ha, ha, ha! Life is so funny! I want the funny man to stay. Ha, ha, ha! Oh, ha, ha, ha!

[*The King speaks to Jack.*]

King: Sir, you have made the Princess laugh. Your reward is her hand in marriage and one half the kingdom.

Jack: Well now, I told Mother so! How surprised she'll be!

Guard: Hurrah for the Princess! Hurrah for Prince Jack!

[*Jack drops the goose to bow over the hand of the Princess, which she holds out to him. At once the unhappy five, set free, drop their arms and join in the shout.*]

All: Hurrah! Hurrah! Hurrah!

— KATHARINE DUNCAN MORSE (*Adapted*).

Who Said It?

Write on a paper the numbers from 1 to 20. Read the quotations on this page and on page 258. After the number of each, write the name of the person who spoke the words. The names of the speakers are given in a list after the quotations. Some names will need to be used more than once.

1. "Only listen while I tell you a funny story."
2. "She does nothing but moan and sigh."
3. "Did you ever see such a sight! Oh, what a joke!"
4. "The meat is roasting on the spit; it will burn to a cinder."
5. "But my dear man, you mustn't go off like that."
6. "If you ever have as much as a dozen copper pennies, that's all I ask."
7. "The bread is in the oven and it will burn if I don't take it out."
8. "You have done an old man a good turn, and don't think you shall lose by it."
9. "I'll have the whole lot of you hanged unless you stop at once."
10. "Does she never laugh at all?"

11. "He says he has brought a goose for Your Majesty."

12. "Did you ever see as funny a face as this?"

13. "I am as hungry as a bear."

14. "I'll go and bring a new loaf for your worship."

15. "She has never been known to laugh since she was born."

16. "Hush! the young man is growing sleepy."

17. "Since I am a rich man, I think I'll go to court and see the King."

18. "Sir, it is plain that you are wasting your breath."

19. "This is too distressing. Nothing seems to do any good."

20. "Do a good day's work and come home to-night with honest wages in your pocket."

Jack
Jack's Mother
An Old Man
The Landlord
The Landlord's Wife
The Landlord's Daughter
The Sexton
The Clerk
The King
The Queen
The Princess
The Doctor
The Herald
Count Nimblewit
Prince Vivien

Things to Do

1. The play, "The Golden Goose," is taken from a book named *Goldtree and Silvertree*, by Katharine Duncan Morse. Some of the other plays in the book are just as amusing as "The Golden Goose." You will enjoy reading them. It is usually more fun to read plays aloud, with different people reading the different parts, than just to read them by one's self.

2. Perhaps you would like to give the play "The Golden Goose" to entertain another class or your mothers and fathers. If you do this, you will need some committees — one to decide who are to take the different parts, another to arrange about the stage and the scenery, another to plan the costumes. It will be a good idea to have some music before and after the play and between the acts. You will need a committee to arrange for that. Perhaps another committee will be needed to take care of the invitations. It will be a good plan also to have some posters made to announce the play and tell when it is to be.

3. It would be fine if you could work together and write a play of your own from one of the stories you have read. Then you could play it.

CLOVERS

The clovers have no time to play.
They feed the cows, and make the hay,

And trim the lawns, and help the bees,
Until the sun sinks through the trees;

And then they lay aside their cares,
And fold their hands to say their prayers,

And drop their tired little heads,
And go to sleep in clover beds.

Then when the day dawns clear and blue,
They wake and wash their hands in dew;

And as the sun climbs up the sky,
They hold them up and let them dry,

And then to work the live-long day;
For clovers have no time to play.

— HELENA LEEMING JELLIFFE.

VII

CHILDREN IN OTHER LANDS

A MOLASSES-CAKE STORY

1. Molasses Cakes and a Joke

Inger Johanne was a little girl who lived in Norway. Her name is pronounced like this, In′-ger Yo-hahn′nuh. She was very lively and got into a good deal of mischief without really meaning to do so. She has written some stories about herself and this is one of them.

Every one in our town says that Mrs. Simonsen's molasses cakes are the best in the world — they are so thick and soft and tasty. Mrs. Simonsen doesn't make them herself — Heinrich Schulze, the head baker, does that. But she stands behind the counter in her shop and sells them every day.

Mrs. Simonsen came from Telemarken. She married the baker Simonsen, and he died and ever since then Heinrich Schulze has been the head baker.

Although I have known Mrs. Simonsen such a long time, there is no use in my going into her shop without money, you may be sure. But whenever I have money, I go there and buy molasses cakes.

If I have no money, I go in the back way through the gate and beg some cake from Heinrich Schulze. As a matter of fact, I go oftenest the back way.

I can almost always find him in the yard there. He is usually hurrying to and fro between the shop and the bakery, and often the molasses cake dough hangs over his shoulder like a long sausage.

Schulze says that good molasses cake dough should be so tough that it will hang over one's shoulder without breaking. Some people think it is disgusting for him to carry the dough that way, but I don't. I even eat it raw, right from his shoulder, very often.

For Schulze and I are great friends, let me tell you. He is German, and is rather old and small. He has black eyes and is very wide-awake, and quick.

I know just exactly the days when he bakes molasses cakes; and on those days I hang around the door and tease. I say, "Please give me a little dough, Schulze, just a little piece, Schulze"; and he almost always gives me some.

One Thursday afternoon (my, how well I remember it!), Schulze, with the dough over his shoulder, came swinging out into the back yard where I sat on a barrel waiting. It happened that I had in my hand a tiny china doll, one of those little "bath dolls" without any clothes on.

Schulze was in a grand good humor that day.

"It may happen that I shall some day be master of this bakery here. Then Heinrich Schulze will be on the top and can snap his fingers at the whole wide world," said Schulze, with the dough over his shoulder and snapping his fingers in the air as he spoke. I think what made him so happy was that Mrs. Simonsen had been extra kind to him and he thought she would probably marry him. Then he would be the master of the bakery.

I don't know how I happened to think of it, but while Schulze stood there talking, I stuck that little china doll right into the dough. Schulze didn't notice what I was doing. I smoothed over the place where I had poked the doll in; and, a moment after, Schulze went into the bake-house.

"What fun it will be when he finds the doll in the dough!" I thought. "He won't be the least bit angry; he will only laugh." So I sat still on the barrel and waited, but he didn't come back.

"Oh, well," I thought, "he just wants to fool me; he must have found the doll."

I stole over to the bake-house door. The molasses cakes were in the pans, ready to be put into the oven that minute.

Schulze never likes to have any one come into the bake-house; so I dared not go further than the door. Not a word did he say about the doll. He was surely trying to fool me into thinking he had not found it. Suddenly I remembered that I had not studied my lessons; so I started on a run for home.

That whole evening I laughed to myself every time I thought of the doll in the cake-dough. I would get the little thing back from Schulze in the morning. But he said not a word about it then, either. He didn't act as if he knew about any joke.

Suppose he hadn't found the doll! Suppose it was baked in a cake and sold, and should get into some one's stomach and the person should be very ill!

That was a dreadful thought, and I grew frightened, oh! so frightened. But I didn't dare say a word to anyone about it. Mrs. Simonsen and Schulze would both be furious if they knew what I had done; and perhaps some one in the town was sick in bed to-day — very, very sick — all because of that molasses cake with my little china doll in it!

Oh, how I did suffer that day! I begged Father for some money and spent it all on molasses cakes. I thought perhaps the little doll might be in one of those I bought. No such good luck. I ate so many molasses cakes, I got perfectly sick of them. I ate them with despair in my heart.

At last I went and stood beside the steps of Mrs. Simonsen's shop and stared at everyone who came out who had bought molasses cakes.

"Perhaps it is you who will get the doll in your stomach — or perhaps it is you," I kept thinking. But if it had been to save my life, I could not have said anything to them even though I was so worried.

When children bought the cakes, however, I took their cakes, whether they liked it or not and squeezed them to find out whether the doll was inside. No, I did not find it.

At last I felt really sick, I was so anxious. Several times I was on the point of going in and telling Mrs. Simonsen; but that would have been very difficult. I couldn't muster up courage enough to do it.

2. The Lost Is Found

The day dragged on. At night I dreamed of the doll in the cake and in the afternoon, when I came from school, I sat down again on the steps of the bakery. Mrs. Simonsen stood in the doorway, sunning herself.

"It is warm and pleasant these days," said Mrs. Simonsen.

Yes, I, too, thought it was very warm. Indeed, I broke into a perspiration whenever I thought of the molasses cake with the doll in it.

"Why, true as you live, if there isn't the Collector of the Port himself coming here," exclaimed Mrs. Simonsen. "He's even coming into the shop, I declare! Go away from the steps, child."

The Collector of the Port is a very important person. So, of course, Mrs. Simonsen was pleased to have him come to her shop.

Yes, the old Collector was really coming up

the walk, with his keen face, his bent back, and his cap with broad gold braid on it. He stopped beside the steps, stuck his cane between the paving-stones and looked up at Mrs. Simonsen in the doorway.

"Is this Mrs. Simonsen who sells molasses cakes?"

Mrs. Simonsen curtsied.

"Yes, your honor," she answered, politely.

The old wooden steps creaked under the Collector's heavy tread. Now he was in the shop. I peeped in at the door.

"May I then ask you, my good woman," said the Collector, "what you call this?"

He searched in one vest pocket, searched a long time — searched in the other vest pocket; and then between his crooked thumb and big pointer finger, he held high in the air my little china doll!

The instant I saw it, I was awfully, awfully glad, for now I knew no one had swallowed it, and that it wasn't lying in anyone's stomach causing pain if not death.

"What do you call this?" repeated the Collector, staring in a terrifying way at Mrs. Simonsen from under his bushy eyebrows.

There was a blank look in Mrs. Simonsen's sky-blue eyes as she looked from the doll to the Collector and from the Collector to the doll. He had to ask her three times before she answered.

"That — that is a — a doll," said Mrs. Simonsen at last, so frightened that she was ready to sink to the floor.

"Yes, perfectly true — a doll. But then may I ask what a doll had to do in my molasses cake? What has it to do there, I ask you? Tell me that."

"In your molasses cake?" exclaimed Mrs. Simonsen in the utmost astonishment. It seemed, however, as if she were a little braver now that the talk came to molasses cakes. There she felt herself surer.

"Yes, right in the molasses cake," snapped the Collector. "I sat drinking my coffee and eating my cake, when I suddenly felt something sc-r-runch between my teeth. I came very near getting it in my throat and choking to death — and that molasses cake came from you," concluded the Collector, putting his silver-mounted cane right against Mrs. Simonsen's breast as if it were a pistol.

"Has the Collector found a doll in his

molasses cake?" cried Mrs. Simonsen in dismay.

"Exactly, Mrs. Simonsen — a doll in my molasses cake."

Then there was a great to-do! Schulze was called from the bake-house and in his baker's cap and apron stood there talking German and insisting that he knew nothing about the doll. The Collector scolded and scolded, and Mrs. Simonsen never got any further than to say, "But, your honor, your esteemed highness —" before the Collector interrupted her with, "Keep still, I say. It is I who will talk."

Oh, how frightened I was! Several times I was about to spring in and say that the doll was mine and that it was I who had put it in the dough, but I didn't dare.

"I will give you notice, my good woman, that hereafter no cakes for me shall be bought here," said the Collector and he struck his cane on the floor with great emphasis.

When he said that, I felt so sorry for Mrs. Simonsen and nice kind Heinrich Schulze that before I knew it, I was in the bakery.

"Oh, it was I who did it! It was I who put the doll into the dough, — just for fun — just for a joke on Schulze. Oh, I have been so sorry about it — oh, hu, hu!" I threw myself down across the counter and lay there, crying and sobbing; but it was a relief to have told at last.

"Well, I must say!" exclaimed the old Collector, but his tone and manner had changed. "Is it here we have the sinner? And you did that for fun? For *fun?*"

"Yes, I thought Schulze would find it right away," I sobbed.

"Whose child are you?" asked the Collector. I told him my father's name without raising my head from the counter.

"H'm, h'm." The Collector cleared his throat. "Well, well. Let it pass, my good Mrs. Simonsen. I shall, after all, go on buying my molasses cakes here. They are exactly to my taste. And you, child" — he tapped my head with the silver head of his cane — "you must find some other kind of fun than putting dolls into molasses cakes for people to choke on." With that the Collector stamped heavily out of the shop.

Mrs. Simonsen was angry with me and so was Schulze; but I was so glad to have the doll in my hands again, so glad that no one had died from it, and that I had eased my conscience by confessing — oh, I can't say how glad I was!

"Please don't be angry," I said. "I did it just for a joke, you know. I will never, never do anything like that again. No, indeed, indeed I will not."

But what do you think? Somehow, since that time, I don't feel like going as often as I used to into Mrs. Simonsen's shop or into the back yard to see Schulze; and I scarcely ever get a bit of molasses cake any more.

I was perfectly disgusted that my splendid joke should have turned out not to be funny at all; but the doll that was baked in a molasses cake and all but swallowed by the Collector of the Port I still keep with my treasures.

— DIKKEN ZWILGMEYER (*Adapted*).

YES OR NO?

Write on a paper the numbers from 1 to 20. Read the sentences on this page. If a sentence agrees with the story, write *Yes* after the number on your paper. If a sentence does not agree with the story, write *No* after its number.

I

1. Inger Johanne lived in Sweden.
2. She was a quiet, mournful child.
3. She was very fond of going to a grocery store to get molasses candy.
4. Heinrich Schulze sometimes carried dough over his shoulder.
5. Everyone thought that this was a very neat thing to do and that it improved the dough.

6. One day Inger Johanne hid a little china doll in the molasses cake dough.

7. She was sure Schulze would never find the doll.

8. Schulze took the doll out of the dough and gave it to Mrs. Simonsen.

9. Inger Johanne became very much worried when Schulze said nothing about the doll.

10. She was worried because she wanted the doll to play with.

11. She stood by the steps of the shop and stared at everyone who had bought molasses cakes.

12. When children came out with cakes, she took the cakes and ate them.

II

13. At last the Collector of the Port came to the shop.

14. He came in a large red automobile.

15. The Collector of the Port had found the missing doll.

16. He was very much pleased and came to give Mrs. Simonsen a reward.

17. Schulze was called in to talk to the Collector.

18. Inger Johanne went into the shop and told what she had done.

19. The Collector told her she must find some other kind of fun.

20. Inger Johanne threw the little china doll into a river.

THINGS TO DO

1. If you would like to read more about Inger Johanne, you will find other stories about her in *Inger Johanne's Lively Doings* by Dikken Zwilgmeyer. The same author has also written an interesting book about a boy in Norway. It is named *Johnny Blossom.*

2. Here is a list of words that describe. Some of these words describe Inger Johanne and some describe the Collector of the Port. Make two lists on a paper, one for Inger Johanne and one for the Collector. Put the names at the head of the lists.

lively	young
quick-tempered	active
bent	heavy
mischievous	merry
thoughtless	friendly
elderly	severe
jolly	stern
warm-hearted	fun-loving

THE WATER BUFFALO'S BATH

Tse Ching was a Chinese boy. The first part of his name is pronounced as if it were spelled Zer; the last part is pronounced just as it is spelled.

Tse Ching worked all day to help his father, but the work was almost like play to the little boy. Tse Ching took care of a big water buffalo, who was old and gentle and slow.

Buffalo deserved good care for she was a great help to Tse Ching's father, with the plowing and other work. She was big, and she hated hot weather, so during the long summertime Tse Ching took her to cool places, under willow trees, or by the wide moat around the city, and stayed with her all day.

It might have been tiresome to lead Buffalo, but Tse Ching didn't do that. He rode on

her wide, gray back, in the deep hollows on either side of it. He was such a small boy that he could sit in one hollow and curl his feet in the hollow on the other side of Buffalo's sharp backbone. Then with a string that went from her nose back across her head to his hand, he guided her along the road.

She usually went where she pleased, and she was so old and had such kind brown eyes that no one thought of bumping her off the road. If she needed to be turned away from some poor feeding place to a grassy hill, Tse Ching just jerked the nose string and Buffalo moved at once.

One morning when it was very hot, Buffalo and Tse Ching started early to find a place cooler than the unshaded plot of ground near their home. The sky was bright and there was no single puff of wind to cool them. Buffalo was so hot that her thick tongue hung out of her mouth and she breathed so heavily that her great sides heaved in and out.

Tse Ching wasn't any too cool, either, though his single coat and trousers were thin. It felt as if it would be a very hot day, indeed, he thought, as he led Buffalo out of her shed and climbed to her back. Just before they started off, Tse Ching saw his pet bird, Bager — his name rhymes with *major* — sitting on his perch. Bager was flapping his wings up and down to show that he was uncomfortable, too.

" Why, Bager," called Tse Ching, " are you hot, sitting on your stick in the shade of the wall and doing nothing? I get hot tugging at Buffalo's rope to make her move out of the shed, and Buffalo gets hot because she is so big and there is so much of her in the sun. But you are little, Bager, and your black wings and shining feathers look very cool."

Bager lifted his wings high and opened his yellow beak to call, " Caw, caw." He acted most certainly as if he were far warmer than either Buffalo or Tse Ching.

" Buffalo," said Tse Ching, " would you mind if I took my bird with me? I should like to, very much, and he could sit on his stick in my hand while I sat on your back. May I take him? "

Buffalo swung her tail to take care of some mischievous flies on her back legs, moved her great, gentle head until she touched Tse Ching's legs, and seemed to say as she rolled her brown eyes, " Nothing matters, my dear, nothing at all, if only you hurry. I do want to get out of this hot sun and I want a drink and a cool bath."

So Tse Ching climbed down and took Bager on his stick. He looked to see that the nose string which was used to guide Buffalo was secure, and then he climbed upon her wide back without spilling Bager. They started off, jogging and dipping as Buffalo moved her heavy feet. Tse Ching liked to ride this way and he knew how to let his body ride loosely and swing with Buffalo's strange gait.

Bager was not used to this strange movement. Once, long ago, he had flown. That was before he had come to be Tse Ching's pet. Once, too, he had been carried to the market by Tse Ching's oldest brother, but he did not know quite how to keep his balance on this morning's ride. He kept slipping and spreading his wings to right himself, then squawking in dismay as he straightened his wings only to tumble off in the other direction.

Tse Ching was happy, for he was cooler now. Before he knew it they had come to the edge of the moat around the outside of the city wall. The bank was slippery because people came here to fill their pails with water, but Buffalo was so hot and thirsty that she slid down the bank with Tse Ching and Bager still on her back, and waded through the shallow water to the middle of the moat.

There the water was cool and deep and Buffalo sank down until only the top of her back and her wet, shining nose showed above it. How fine she felt to be covered with water and cool at last! She drank long and loudly, closed her eyes, and rested.

Tse Ching drew his feet up under him and was safe and dry on Buffalo's back. He had often sat there for hours while she rested, but Bager was afraid of the water. He did not like water at all; so he flapped his wings, and that made Buffalo very nervous. She reached up her tail, as if Bager had been some huge fly, and splashed water on him to make him go away.

Of course, the water didn't stick on Bager's black feathers; but, since he hated water, it made him very angry. He cawed loudly and hopped along his stick close to Tse Ching to hide against his coat.

"Poor bird," said Tse Ching. "I am sorry about the water, but Buffalo doesn't like you to make that noise, and she really didn't know how you felt about water, I am sure. Here, let me see if you are really wet." Tse Ching reached up the hand that held the nose string, and just then Buffalo wriggled and nearly dumped them off into the moat.

"Hey, Buffalo," called Tse Ching, "be still or we shall all be dumped into the water. You know I can't swim!" But now Buffalo was cross. There was too much talking and fussing on her back, she thought. She muttered to herself and started out to the very deepest water.

Tse Ching knew that the water farther out was too deep, and the moat bottom slippery with mud. So he reached to pull the nose string and direct Buffalo to a shallower place. But there was no string in his hand, no string resting on the small dry space on Buffalo's back! On and on walked Buffalo, floundering and sliding, and Tse Ching had no way to bring her back.

"Oh say, Bager," cried Tse Ching, "I must have dropped the nose string when I reached up to dry your wings, and I can't find it, and I don't know what to do. Buffalo is so slippery where she is wet that I can't climb nearer her head and reach over her face to find the other end. What shall I do?"

Bager was helpless, too, and Buffalo went farther and farther. Her feet spread and slid in the mud, but Tse Ching could not turn her head. Just then a small breeze came by as if to laugh at the strange boat a buffalo made. As it passed by, it smoothed the moat and Tse Ching saw the nose string floating out beyond his reach. He had to have that string to turn Buffalo.

He thought quickly and remembered a trick of Bager's that might help. If Tse Ching held something a little distance from Bager and told him to fly for it, the bird would fly as far as the string on his foot would let him.

"Do you suppose, Bager, that you could reach the string if I held you far out over the water?" asked Tse Ching. Bager did not answer, but — Tse Ching, holding his breath and stretching his arm far out over the water, said, "Reach out, pet bird, reach out."

Bager looked up. He saw nothing above him to reach, and nothing lay on either side; but there, below him, in the hated cold water, lay a string. He shivered slightly and lifted his wings as Tse Ching called softly, "Reach out, reach out." He flew down close to the water, dipped in his beak, and pulled the

nose string out and over to where Tse Ching clung to the angry Buffalo's back.

Tse Ching straightened himself and snatched the string. He jerked it stoutly and Buffalo turned obediently as if she had been waiting for a sign as to when her bath must end. Bager came back to his stick and preened himself and shook out his feathers. He was proud and pleased.

Tse Ching was pleased, too. When Buffalo had landed them safely on the bank again and was resting under a willow tree, Tse Ching took Bager to a rice field near by and let him nip at the new, green shoots at the edge of the field. Soon Bager was full of his favorite dinner and ready to puff up his black throat and sing.

— DOROTHY ROWE (*Adapted*).

IMPROVE THE ORDER

These sentences are not in the right order. Read them over and decide what the right order should be. Write on a paper the numbers of the sentences so as to show the correct order. The first number to put down is 7, for sentence 7 should come first.

1. That day the little boy took Bager, his pet bird, with him on Buffalo's back.
2. Tse Ching and Bager were frightened, but Bager flew down to the water and picked up the nose string in his beak.
3. One morning when it was very hot, Buffalo and Tse Ching started early.
4. Buffalo splashed water on Bager with her tail.

5. Bager flapped his wings because he did not like the water and this made Buffalo nervous.

6. Tse Ching reached up his hand to see if Bager was wet and dropped Buffalo's nose string.

7. Tse Ching was a little Chinese boy who took care of a big water buffalo.

8. Instead of leading Buffalo, Tse Ching rode on her wide, gray back and guided her by a nose string.

9. Bager kept slipping, and spreading his wings to right himself, and squawking in dismay.

10. In summer, Tse Ching took her to cool places under willow trees or by the wide moat.

11. When they reached the moat, Buffalo went into the water till only her back and head showed.

12. Buffalo deserved good care for she was a great help to Tse Ching's father.

THINGS TO DO

1. The story about Tse Ching is taken from a book by Dorothy Rowe, named *Traveling Shops*. If you read *Traveling Shops* and like it, you will probably enjoy two other books about China by the same author — *The Rabbit Lantern* and *The Moon's Birthday*.

2. Write on a paper the numbers from 1 to 20. In each line — not column — on page 293, there is

one word that is the same in meaning, or almost the same, as the first word in the line. Pick out each of these words and write it after the number of its line. For example, you will write first *1. annoyed,* because *annoyed* has almost the same meaning as *angry*.

1.	angry	loud	plenty	annoyed
2.	beak	bill	bone	pole
3.	black	blue	iron	dark
4.	breeze	cloud	wind	kite
5.	dismay	alarm	sorrow	pleasure
6.	distance	walk	road	space
7.	dumped	held	gave	unloaded
8.	guided	led	helped	started
9.	hot	cooked	warm	brown
10.	shivered	moved	trembled	shouted
11.	slow	unhurried	quiet	elderly
12.	squawking	walking	flying	crying
13.	strange	ugly	impolite	unusual
14.	secure	fine	new	safe
15.	shining	beautiful	yellow	glistening
16.	sharp	bright	keen	little
17.	tugging	pulling	holding	helping
18.	mischievous	wild	noisy	naughty
19.	preened	washed	painted	smoothed
20.	uncomfortable	rough	uneasy	pretty

LITTLE TONINO

1. Tonino's Home

If you went to France, and got into an automobile, and drove up and up along a winding white road straight into the mountains, you might come to a little gray old town on the top of a cliff with a high wall all around it. Here you would have to leave the automobile and walk up a steep, cobbled street that would lead you to the gate of the old town. The name of the old town is Nouvilo. It is pronounced Noo-vee-lo.

Nouvilo means *new town.* I haven't a doubt that seven or eight hundred years ago Nouvilo really *was* new, and the houses stood upright, and were white and shining. But now Nouvilo is very old indeed, so old that the houses are all crooked and seem to lean against each other. They are too old to stand upright! In the very crookedest house of all lives a little boy called Tonino. You say his name like this — Toe-nee'no.

The back of Tonino's house bulges over the town wall, which grows right out of the side of the cliff. The front door of Tonino's house opens on a little narrow street. It is so narrow that if a donkey cart comes along you have to climb somebody's doorstep to get out of the way!

Tonino's house has two front doors. One is very narrow and leads up some corkscrew stone steps to the kitchen. The kitchen is very big. It is both kitchen and living room. Next to the kitchen is a smaller room where Tonino's grandmother and his sister, Nanou, sleep. (You say *Nanou* like this — Nan-oo'.) Another flight of corkscrew stairs leads up to a big bedroom. This belongs to Tonino's father and mother. Next to the big bedroom is a tiny little room that is Tonino's own.

The other front door is very wide and leads into a large room level with the street. And here live all the animals except the big, gray cat, who sleeps in the kitchen. There's Lavanda, the goat, and there's the proud rooster with beautiful green tail-feathers, and there are seven hens, and ever so many chickens. Here also live Mignonetto, the big mother donkey, and her little boy donkey Tintourlet. You pronounce these names Min-yun-et'toe and Tan-toor-lay'.

Tintourlet is Tonino's very own donkey.

Tonino named him. The name means "little and sweet and darling."

Tintourlet was nearly grown up now. He could carry light loads on his back. Every day when Tonino's family went out to their little farm that was nearly a mile from the town, Tonino rode on Tintourlet's back a part of the way. Nanou had a turn, too. Tonino's father and mother always walked, but his grandmother drove in the little donkey cart that Mignonetto drew.

When they came to the farm, Mignonetto was tethered to one tree and Tintourlet to another. Then they wandered around and around, nibbling the delicious grass while Tonino and Nanou and their father and mother and grandmother worked hard in the vineyards and among the terraces.

For Tonino's father and mother were farmers, though they did not live on their farms as farmers do in America. No, they lived in their house in the village; and every

day, as soon as it was light, they went out to work on the farm. That is the way it is done in France. And what do you think they grew on their farm?

They did not grow wheat or rye or corn. No, indeed. Tonino's father and his mother and his grandmother had a flower farm. They grew roses and gillyflowers and stocks and carnations and violets. They had besides a vineyard, where grapes grew, and an orange orchard.

There was a big barn on the farm, but the farmhouse was tiny, with only two rooms. It was built on the side of a hill. You could jump from the last terrace of the vineyard at the back onto the roof. Tonino often did this, and so did Minou, the cat.

At the front of the house was the orchard of orange trees. These also grew on terraces, row upon row, until the orchard ended where the road passed through the farm. On the other side of the road were more terraces where the flowers were planted — the roses and carnations and violets and lots of other sweet-smelling flowers.

In March, and the months following, when most of the flowers were in bloom, there would be a flower harvest, and the flowers would be taken to a big perfume factory to be made into perfume or used in scented soap.

During the school year Tonino and Nanou did not work among the flowers except on Saturday, because they had to go to school. Their grandmother stayed in the town then too, to cook their noon meal. Their father and mother had theirs on the farm — a picnic lunch of bread and cheese and cold sausage.

Tonino's grandmother was a dear old lady. She always dressed in black on week days, with a little black shawl and a big blue apron. She always wore a close-fitting white bonnet. When she went out she put a big black hat on top of her bonnet. The children always called her *Mameto*, which is pronounced Mah-may'toe and means "little mother."

Mameto knew any number of stories. When something reminded her of one she would begin, "Once upon a time." Then Tonino and Nanou would sit right down beside her and any child who happened to be in the street would hurry there too, in order not to miss a word.

At eleven o'clock, Tonino and Nanou always came running home from school. They would find Mameto sitting on their front step knitting a sock for Tonino or Nanou or for their father and chatting to the other old ladies who lived in the same street. Always when she saw them coming she would call out, "Tonino, run upstairs and get the green jugs and get some water from the fountain."

Because, what do you think? There was no water in Tonino's house! No, indeed, and there was not a single house in Nouvilo that had water! Nor did people have wells in their back yards. All the people in the town had to take their pitchers or their pails and get their water at the big fountain in the square near the church.

All day long you would see people going to the fountain with empty pitchers or coming back with full ones.

Tonino really liked very much his job of getting water from the fountain. As the

fountain was on the Big Square — a kind of park — he was sure to meet somebody that he knew, either fetching water, too, or washing vegetables or going to market or coming home.

Here also was the blacksmith's shop, and Tonino liked to stop a minute to watch the smith shoeing a donkey or beating nails on the anvil.

2. The Town Wall and the Castle

I have already told that the little old town of Nouvilo had a wall around it. There were two gates in this wall. It was only through one gate or the other that you could get into Nouvilo at all.

The bigger gate opened onto a drawbridge that crossed the ravine. But the drawbridge had not been drawn up for hundreds of years now. Robbers no longer ride around the country attacking cities and plundering them, as they used to do when Nouvilo was first built.

It must have been a clever enemy who could get into Nouvilo with its drawbridge pulled up. At such times, all the men of the town stood with bows drawn behind the little arrow holes in the city walls, ready to shoot at the enemy.

The other gate was called the "postern gate," and it opened on a very old road paved with cobblestones. There were steps every few feet; so the road was like a long winding stairway leading down into the valley. Here the water from the fountain ran beside the road in an open stone-lined gutter and was used to water all the little farms in the valley. It was along this road that Tonino's father and mother and Lavanda, the goat, and Mignonetto and Tintourlet walked every morning on the way to the farm.

The narrow little street that Tonino lived in was at the edge of the town. His house looked over the city wall. All the streets in Nouvilo were just as narrow, and the houses bulged out in the second story so that they nearly touched. Sometimes a house would be built right across the street from the second story of one house to the second story of the one opposite.

Of course these houses had been built ever so long ago when people did not think it safe to live outside the walls of the town. So when there was no more room to build on the ground some one got the bright idea of building an arch across the street and building his house on top of the arch — and others did the same.

Out of the Big Square, another street led still farther uphill to an old castle with four turrets, one on each corner. Here in the olden days lived the Counts of Nouvilo and their court of knights and ladies and long-haired pages and men at arms. But there had been no Count of Nouvilo now for more than a hundred years, and the castle belonged to the town of Nouvilo. What do you think it was used for?

You never could guess, because it seems an odd use for a castle. The old castle was now the schoolhouse. The only people who lived there were the schoolmaster and his wife. Here every morning at eight o'clock Tonino and Nanou and all the other children of Nouvilo came to school. In order not to be late, they all had to get up at half-past six!

3. The Morning

Every morning, the minute that Tonino heard his father knock on the wall, he jumped out of bed and washed himself in his little basin and put on his clothes quickly. He wore a little blue shirt, and trousers with green suspenders, and an orange slipover sweater, for Tonino's mother liked bright colors. Last of all he put on his black school apron, for every boy and every girl who went to school had to wear such aprons. Most of the children wore them all day and every day except Sunday.

After Tonino had brushed his short black hair he hurried down to the stable to give Mignonetto and Tintourlet their breakfast and to watch his father milking Lavanda, the goat. When Lavanda had given all her milk, Tonino ran up to the kitchen with the little pail full of creamy milk and put it on the kitchen table. Then his mother could prepare the breakfast chocolate over the

charcoal fire, while his father went to the fountain with two enormous water pails.

By this time Mignonetto and Tintourlet had finished their breakfast. Tonino had just time to harness Mignonetto to her little cart and put the bridle on Tintourlet before Nanou came running back from the bakeshop with the bread for breakfast.

It was an enormous loaf of bread that Nanou carried, very narrow but nearly as long as Tonino. Nanou loved her morning job. The jolly woman who kept the bakeshop was a great friend of hers, and the big plump cat that generally sat on the counter had once been one of Minou's kittens.

Then the whole family would sit down to breakfast in the big kitchen with the fire burning in the fireplace under the great hooded chimney. It was a comfortable kitchen with a red-tiled floor and three big chairs — one for Tonino's father, one for his mother, one for his grandmother — and two little chairs for Tonino and Nanou. On the window sill there were pots of pink geranium. As he sat at the table, Tonino could look out of the window and see the hills and farms far away on the other side of the valley.

Breakfast was a delicious meal — fresh crusty bread, still warm from the bakeshop, and big bowls of hot chocolate.

As soon as breakfast was finished, Tonino's mother climbed into the donkey cart and his father took Tintourlet by the bridle, and they started off for the farm with Lavanda following them.

As for Tonino and Nanou, *they* had to hurry off to school, for it would be terrible to be late. So they climbed the street to the castle and went in at the big front door. Then they had to climb a flight of stairs to get to their schoolroom. What a huge flight of stairs it was, all built of stone!

On the school landing there were two big rooms divided by a hall. In this hall were rows of hooks on which the children hung their berets and capes. The room on the right belonged to the big boys, and the room on the left to the girls and to the little boys. As Tonino was only seven years old, he still belonged in the girls' room with Nanou. He was in the second division of the primary class, and next year he would be promoted to the big boys' room.

As the clock struck eight the head teacher, and his wife, who taught the girls, came down the stairs from their apartment on the floor above, and the children formed themselves into groups according to their classes. The two teachers started to sing a marching song, and all the children joined in and sang as they marched. The older boys went into one room and the girls and little boys into the other, and they all took their places at their desks.

Then everyone was very busy until eleven o'clock. When the church bell struck eleven, all the children jumped up and marched into the hall singing:

"On we go,
On we go,
In spite of
The driving snow,
If sometimes
Things will go ill,
Don't let's fear
The wintry chill!"

This was rather a joke, for it hardly ever snowed in Nouvilo. Even in December, the sun shone brightly and it was often so warm that the children did not need to wear their capes to school!

Soon the little narrow streets were full of boys and girls running home, ready to run errands for their mothers, to lay the table, or to get water from the fountain and help to get their dinner ready. I have already told you that getting water from the fountain was Tonino's particular job, and he and Nanou always helped their grandmother to peel the potatoes or shell the peas.

4. The Afternoon

Now I'll tell you what Tonino and Nanou had for dinner. Nearly always it was soup. But such delicious soup, made with meat and carrots and turnips and squash, and eggplant when it was in season, and always potatoes. Then afterwards there was spinach or green peas or beans with hard-boiled eggs, and sometimes a bowl of salad, too.

Only on Sundays did they eat meat. One reason for that was that charcoal stoves do not have ovens! But, all the same, every Sunday Mameto served a delicious dinner of roast veal with roasted potatoes and baked squash or stuffed peppers or eggplants.

How do you think that meat got roasted without an oven? I will tell you. On Sunday morning just before church, Mameto gave Nanou a basket, with the veal all ready in an earthenware pot, surrounded by the potatoes nicely peeled, and also a flat pan with the tomatoes or squash or peppers.

Nanou carried it to the bakery. There she would find a crowd of people all bringing their Sunday dinners to be baked or roasted in the big bakery oven.

Then at twelve o'clock Mameto herself went to bring it home. She was always afraid that Nanou might burn herself with the earthenware pot, all piping hot as it came out of the oven.

Sometimes they had roast chicken for dinner. But that was only on great feast days like Christmas or New Year's Day, or the Fourteenth of July, which is almost exactly like our Fourth of July, for all little French boys and girls.

After dinner Tonino and Nanou always washed the dinner dishes, and then they ran off to the school yard to have a game of rounders or prisoners' base or cavaliers before afternoon school began.

Cavaliers was a game that the schoolboys liked very much. Perhaps a dozen boys would play at a time. Six of them would stand with their hands on their knees. The other six mounted their backs and began to toss a ball around. They were cavaliers. If any cavalier missed his catch he had to get down and pick up the ball. Then *he* had to become the horse and his horse became the cavalier.

Tonino and the other smaller boys and girls only had to stay at school till half-past two, but they were allowed to stay till half-past three if they wanted to. On rainy days they generally did want to, for then their teacher would tell them stories and show them how to cut out little animals from colored paper. The best animals were pasted on long strips

of brown paper and used to decorate the schoolroom.

Nanou loved afternoon school. She liked drawing and sewing. She learned how to embroider little mats and doilies with colored threads, which made beautiful New Year's presents to give to her mother and grandmother and her other friends. Also she liked to watch the older girls painting pottery. They were allowed to do this as soon as they had prepared their lessons for the following day.

And what do you think? They really earned money by the painting! In the next village, there was a pottery studio, where a man made cups and saucers and pots and jugs and vases. Several times a year a cart-load of the smaller pieces of pottery would be brought to Nouvilo for the older children to paint and decorate. Then they were taken back to the studio to be baked and the man who made the pottery sold them to an agent. This agent came twice a year from the big towns on the coast to buy pottery for the pottery shops.

If your mother owns some French pottery cups and saucers or bowls, it may be that these same cups and saucers and bowls were decorated by the school children of Nouvilo.

— Helen Hill and Violet Maxwell (*Adapted*).

Find the Right Word

Write on a paper the numbers from 1 to 20. Choose the right word to finish each sentence and write it on your paper after the number of the sentence.

I

1. The name Nouvilo means new
   town, city, village, harbor.

2. The back of Tonino's house bulges over the
   rocks, cliff, street, wall.

3. The front door of Tonino's house opens on a little, narrow
   path, valley, bridge, street.

4. In a room level with the street, live all the
   family, neighbors, animals, children.

5. Tonino's father and mother live in a village and go every day to their
   factory, farm, bakery, store.

6. On the farm, they raise
   flowers, wheat, corn, cabbages.

7. When the children were at school, their grandmother cooked their
   breakfast, supper, noon meal.

8. Every day Tonino took two green jugs and went for

milk, water, coffee, tea.

II

9. The wall around Nouvilo had two

doors, openings, towers, gates.

10. The wall is not used now, but long ago it kept out

bears, panthers, enemies, chickens.

11. The postern gate opened on an old road paved with

cobblestones, bricks, stone, cement.

12. Farther up the hill was an old castle that was used for a

church, school, theater, library.

III

13. Tonino, Nanou, and all the other children wore black

stockings, aprons, coats, sweaters.

14. The children's mother did her cooking over a fire made with

peat, charcoal, coal, wood.

15. For breakfast they had warm bread and big bowls of hot

chocolate, soup, milk, coffee.

16. The children stayed in school till the clock struck

eleven, twelve, one, two.

IV

17. For dinner Tonino and Nanou always had

fish, steak, soup, pudding.

18. On Sunday, the dinner was cooked at the

grocery, drugstore, castle, bakery.

19. In afternoon school some of the older children painted

pictures, boxes, pottery, chairs.

20. They were allowed to paint when they had prepared their

colors, lessons, supper, clothing.

Things to Do

1. The story "Little Tonino" is taken from a book named *Little Tonino* by Helen Hill and Violet Maxwell. If you read it, you will find out a great many interesting things about life in France.

Another good story about France is *Nanette of the Wooden Shoes* by Esther Brann. If you would like to read a story about children in Spain, you will enjoy *Lupe Goes to School.* This is by Esther Brann, too.

2. See if you can find out in what part of France Nouvilo is, so that you can point out on a map just about where it would be.

3. Write six ways in which Tonino's life was different from yours. Write on paper, not in your book. Make a little outline like this:

I. Tonino's Life
   1. Tonino lived in France.
   2.
   3.
   4.
   5.
   6.

II. My Life
   1. I live in America.
   2.
   3.
   4.
   5.
   6.

VIII

WHEELS AND WINGS

IN THE TRAIN

Away through the country
  We hurry so fast
We scarcely can see things
  Before they are passed.

The meadows of daisies,
  The children at play,
The trees and the horses
  They all slip away.

The fences whirl by us;
  The far-away hill
Moves back like a sentinel
  Solemn and still.

And only the thin little
  Moon in the air
Sails silently with us
  And always is there.

— KATHARINE PYLE.

CHARLIE RIDES WITH THE ENGINEER

1. The Train

Charlie and his father and mother and aunt and his puppy, Bingo, were all going to visit the place where Charlie's father had lived when he was a little boy! It would certainly be great fun.

When they got to the station they all went straight through the gate to the platform, and there the train was waiting for them. It was a long train with ever so many coaches.

Charlie and his father took Bingo to the baggage car, and the baggage man fastened Bingo's leash to the end of a trunk. Bingo did not like the baggage car, but he had been in one before; so he was not frightened. Bingo had to have a ticket. Charlie thought he ought to feel pleased about that.

Then they all went into a car and took their seats and the train gave a loud whistle and steamed out of the station. How fast it went! Everything seemed to go flying past.

Soon the conductor came walking down the aisle and punched everybody's ticket. He was tall and stout and wore a blue uniform. He soon came to the seat where Charlie and his father were sitting and punched their tickets. He stuck Charlie's father's ticket in his hatband, but as Charlie's mother and aunt had no hatbands, he stuck their tickets into the top of the seat in front of them.

Then he took Charlie's ticket; and, when he had punched it, he stuck it in Charlie's hatband. Charlie felt very proud and would not take his hat off. He kept his hat on because he wanted everybody to see that *he* had a ticket in his hatband just like all the other men.

Then Charlie said to his father, "Father, what makes the train go?"

His father said, “It’s the steam that makes the engine work, and it is the engineer and the fireman who look after the steam and the engine.” But Charlie said, “I know that; what I want to know is exactly what the fireman and the engineer do when they are making the engine go.”

Charlie’s father did not know exactly what they did. He said that he had never had a ride on an engine in his life, so how could he know what they did? Charlie’s mother and his aunt did not know either.

Well, after they had been in the big train for an hour, they came to a station where there were a lot of tracks. This station was called a *junction.* A junction is a meeting place or a joining place. On the railroad, a junction is a place where tracks meet.

Some of the tracks went to the north and some to the south and some to the east and some to the west. The train that Charlie and his father and mother and aunt were on was going toward the west; but now they wanted to go to the north, so they had to change trains and go on another train that was going toward the north.

The train they wanted was already waiting on its own track. It was a very little train. It had only two coaches!

Charlie's mother and his aunt got into the train, and they took Bingo with them. It was such a little friendly train, the conductor said that Bingo might travel in the day coach instead of staying in the baggage car, and Bingo was very glad to be with the family again. Charlie and his father waited on the platform till it was time for the train to start, and they looked at all the interesting things about them.

A man came up to them. He wore overalls and a peaked cap. And guess who it was! It was the fireman who helped work the engine of the train they were going to take. The fireman knew Charlie's father! He came up to them, and said to Charlie's father, "Hello, Bob!" Charlie's father said, "Why—Hello, Bill," and they shook hands.

Charlie was very much surprised that the fireman and his father knew each other, but it was not so very surprising after all. The fireman lived in the village where Charlie's father had lived when he was a little boy, and where Charlie and his father and mother and aunt were going to live for a month. His father and the fireman had gone to the same school when they were little boys!

Well, the fireman looked at Charlie, and said, "Is this your boy?"

Charlie's father said, "Yes, this is Charlie; and you are the very man he wants to meet. Charlie wants to know exactly what the fireman and the engineer do to make the train go — and he can't find anybody who knows. So go ahead and tell him all about it."

But the fireman said, "I can do better than that. Suppose you and Charlie take a ride on the engine with me. Then he can see everything with his own eyes, and learn all there is to know in case he wants to be a fireman himself."

Yes, the fireman said those very words; and Charlie's father said, "That will be fine. I'll just go and tell Charlie's mother what has become of us, so that she won't worry."

When he had done this, the fireman and Charlie and his father all got into the cab, which is back of the engine, where the engineer and the fireman stay.

3. The Engine

The engineer was already sitting in his place, which is on the right side of the cab. He was very much pleased to meet Charlie and his father, but he said that after the train had started he would not be able to speak a word to anybody, and nobody must speak to him. Nobody must speak to the engineer when he is driving the engine, because talking might distract his attention and then the train might be wrecked.

All the time that the train is going the engineer has to sit in his seat with his left hand on the throttle. The throttle is the lever that lets the steam into the cylinders to make the engine go. When the lever shuts the steam off, the engine has to slow down and stop.

At the engineer's left side is another lever — a little one. This lever sticks out sideways on top of a round box that is on top

of an iron pipe. This is the air-brake control. It is used to stop the train very suddenly if something is on the track.

There is another lever that is moved by a wheel in front of the engineer. It is the reverse lever. When the train is going ahead, the wheel is turned to the right. When the engineer wants to make the train go backward, he turns the wheel the other way.

The engineer has to keep looking ahead out of a window in front of him. If he sees a green signal on a signal post, this means that the engine can go straight ahead, but if the signal he sees is red, then it means "Stop" — and the engineer presses on the throttle, and the train stops.

The engineer told all this to Charlie while they were waiting for the train to start. Then the engineer got the signal from the man on the platform. He blew the whistle, and the train started, and he did not say another word.

The fireman's place is on the left side of the cab, and Charlie and his father sat between the fireman and the window.

The fireman has to work hard, but when he is not working he may talk if he wants to. This fireman was very kind, and, when he was not working, he explained everything to Charlie and his father — but all the time he was explaining he had to keep looking out of the window, too, in case he should see anything that the engineer did not see.

There are a great many windows in the cab of an engine — it has windows all around, because it is so very important that the engineer and the fireman shall see all that they need to see.

Well, I will now tell you what the fireman was doing all the time that Charlie and his father were riding on the engine with him.

In front of the fireman was a steam gauge, which is a round thing like a clock. It has a hand like a clock hand, too, and the steam makes the hand move — so that you can see how much steam is coming out of the boiler. When the steam is getting low the hand drops, and when the hand drops to 150 the fireman knows it is time to put more coal into the fire box.

Every time that the hand of the gauge dropped to 150 the fireman got up and opened a little door in the back of the cab, which

opened right into the fire box so that you could see the fire all red and glowing; and the fireman sent a great shovel full of coal into it. The fireman told Charlie that it is very important how one shovels the coal into the fire box. It has to be shoveled very evenly, so that the fire is not all black with coal in one place and all red hot with embers in another place. The fireman told Charlie that it needs a lot of practice before one can shovel the coal in just right.

Then the fireman also had to watch the water gauge, which shows how much water there is in the boiler.

When he saw by the water gauge that the water was getting low in the boiler, the fireman had to turn a valve, which is a sort of handle that starts a pump working, and the pump pumps water into the boiler.

Charlie wanted to turn the valve himself, but the fireman said, "No," that it needed a whole lot of practice before one could pump water into the tank. If too much cold water is pumped into the boiler it might cool the water already in the boiler so that no more steam would come out — and then the train would stop!

Do you think that the fireman on an engine is a busy man? Indeed he is!

But that is not all the fireman has to do.

Oh, dear, no! The fireman has a lot more work to do.

When the train is coming to an uphill place — and there were a lot of steep places on the road that Charlie was traveling on — the fireman has to make the fire red hot, so that lots and lots of steam can come out of the boiler. He makes the fire get hotter and hotter until the steam gets so strong that the safety valve pops — and this shows the engineer that there is enough steam to push the train up the steep place. You can see that it would need a lot of extra steam to push a train up a steep, high hill.

Once in a while a little whistle would sound in the top of the cab. This was a message from the conductor to the engineer. What the message is can be told by the number of toots the little whistle gives.

The fireman also has to blow a whistle — a bigger whistle — whenever the train comes to a crossing or to a station. Two long blasts followed by two short ones mean "We are coming to a crossing." One long blast means "We are coming to a station." Once they saw a cow on the track. The fireman made the whistle give a great many quick short blasts. The cow seemed to think this meant "Get off the track," for she got off — just in time.

When they got to the last stop — which was the village where Charlie and his mother and father and aunt and Bingo were going to live for a month — the fireman let Charlie blow the whistle himself. And you should have heard what a loud whistle Charlie blew!

Well, at last they had come to the end of their journey, and Charlie certainly had learned a whole lot about engines. He had learned a good deal more than most people know. Of course he told his mother and his aunt about everything, so that they, too, might know all about what the fireman and the engineer do to make the train go.

Charlie said to his mother, "When I get home to the city I shall be able to play that I am the fireman or the engineer, and I will know exactly what they do, and I will practice being an engineer or a fireman so that I can be one when I grow up!"

— HELEN HILL AND VIOLET MAXWELL (*Adapted*).

Yes or No?

Write on a paper the numbers from 1 to 15. If a sentence tells what the story tells, write *Yes* after its number on your paper. If a sentence does not tell what the story tells, write *No* after its number.

I

1. Bingo was frightened because he had never been in a baggage car before.

2. The conductor walked down the aisle without stopping.

3. Charlie's father said he knew exactly what made the train go.

4. They all changed to a little train that had only two coaches.

5. Charlie and his father waited inside the railway station.

6. A fireman came up and spoke to Charlie's father.

7. The fireman said he would let them ride in the engineer's cab.

II

8. While the train was going, Charlie asked the engineer a great many questions.

9. The engineer sat with his right hand on the throttle.

10. A green signal means that the train can go ahead.

11. There were no windows in the engineer's cab.

12. The steam gauge lets the fireman know how much steam is coming out of the boiler.

13. The fireman shoveled coal into the fire box.

14. A little whistle in the top of the cab gave messages to the engineer from the conductor.

15. The fireman blew a louder whistle whenever he felt like it.

Things to Do

1. The story "Charlie Rides with the Engineer," except for some of the facts about the engine, is taken from *Charlie and His Puppy Bingo*, by Helen Hill and Violet Maxwell. If you are interested in trains you will also like to read *The Wonderful Locomotive* by Cornelia Meigs and *Clear Track Ahead*, by Henry B. Lent.

2. Working together, make a list of questions about locomotives that you would like to have answered. Arrange them in good order. Leave out questions that the people in the class can answer. Try to find the answers to the others by talking to people who know about locomotives and by looking in books.

SEEING LINDBERGH OFF

In 1927, when Don Wills was a small boy, he came to live in a place not far from Curtiss Field, on Long Island. Curtiss Field is a great flying field. Don's Uncle Rod was learning to be an aviator and Don became very much interested in flying. He wanted to be a flyer himself, as soon as he was old enough.

One day, Don heard his uncle say something about an aviator who wanted to win the Orteig prize.

"What is the Orteig prize?" asked Don.

"Well," said Uncle Rod, "about eight years ago — it was in 1919 — a Frenchman named Raymond Orteig offered a prize to aviators. He promised to pay twenty-five thousand dollars to the first person who would fly, without stopping, from New

York to Paris or from Paris to New York. You see, Don, Mr. Orteig was born in France, and he lives in America; so he is much interested in a flight between the two countries."

"It's a long way to fly," said Don.

"It certainly is," said his uncle. "Just look it up on your globe."

"Has anyone tried for the prize yet?" asked Don.

" Yes," said Uncle Rod. " Two plucky Frenchmen, Captain Nungesser and Major Coli, started from Paris about a week ago, but they were lost. No trace of them has been found. Another Frenchman, Captain Fonck, started right here at Curtiss Field, but an accident happened and his plane was smashed as he was taking off. An American naval officer named Noel Davis was killed while he was practicing to get ready to fly across."

" Who do you think will try next?" asked Don.

" Several flyers are making plans to go," said Uncle Rod; " but the next one to start will probably be a young man named Charles Lindbergh. He flew from California and landed at Curtiss Field a few days ago. Some people in St. Louis helped him buy his monoplane. It is named the *Spirit of St. Louis.*"

" Who is going to fly to Paris with him?" asked Don.

" He says he is going alone," said Uncle

Rod. " He is only twenty-five years old and some of the newspapers call him ' The Flying Fool,' but he doesn't look like a fool to me. He's been flying a mail airplane between Chicago and St. Louis. Carrying mail is good flying practice, because the men who do it have to fly at night and in all kinds of weather. But Lindbergh certainly can't get to Paris in less than thirty hours, and that's a long time to go without sleep. Of course he can't do any sleeping if he flies alone."

In the next few days, Don asked his uncle a great many questions about the young flyer who was planning to cross the Atlantic alone.

One day Don went to Curtiss Field with his uncle. While he was there, he saw Lindbergh — a tall, slim, strongly built young man with fair hair and blue eyes.

Very early in the morning on the twentieth of May, Don was sleeping soundly, when some one shook him gently.

" G'way," he said.

"Wake up, Don," said his uncle softly "Don't make any noise. Get dressed as soon as you can. Lindbergh is going to start for Paris, and I want you to see him take off. Now for pity's sake don't make any racket and wake your mother and the baby. Bring your raincoat and rubbers."

In a surprisingly short time, Don and his uncle were going softly down stairs in their stocking feet. Soon, with their shoes on, they hopped into Uncle Rod's automobile and were off for Curtiss Field.

After they reached the field, they stood with some other people near the hangar where the *Spirit of St. Louis* was kept. It was very dark, but there were some lights about the hangar and there were a number of automobile headlights showing. Rain was falling in a slow drizzle.

After a time Lindbergh came. They could tell quickly who he was, even in the dim light, because he was so much taller than anyone else there.

Soon the hangar was opened and the *Spirit of St. Louis* was wheeled out on the field with her nose pointing east. Mechanics gave the airplane a last looking over and filled the tanks with gasoline.

"It holds four hundred and fifty-one gallons," Don heard some one say.

Daylight was coming now, and there was less rain.

Lindbergh put on his flying clothes and his helmet. He shook hands with some people near the plane, who wished him good luck. Uncle Rod stepped forward and Lindbergh shook hands with him and with Don, too.

Don could not think of anything to say, but the tall young aviator seemed to understand, for a smile flashed across his face as he looked down at the little boy.

Then Lindbergh stepped into the cabin and took his seat. He looked out at the people standing on the wet field and waved his hand.

"So long," he said.

He opened the throttle and the airplane moved forward along the wet runway. It moved slowly because the wheels sank in the wet ground. The people looking on began to fear that a take-off would not be possible.

But the plane rose, rose above the trees and the telephone poles. Looking, as it flew, like a great silver bird, it passed out of sight in the cloudy morning sky.

Don and his uncle were rather quiet as they rode home. At last Uncle Rod said, "I'm hungry. Aren't you? I'd like about a dozen scrambled eggs."

"Yes," said Don. "Uncle Rod, did Lindbergh take something to eat with him?"

"Two cans of water and a little package of sandwiches," said Uncle Rod, "not much food for a three thousand mile trip, Don, my boy! But, somehow, I think he's going to get there."

"So do I," said Don.

School was hard for Don that day, partly because he was sleepy, but largely because he kept wondering how Lindbergh was getting on. He spent most of Saturday listening to the radio for reports of his hero's progress. When, on Saturday evening, the news came through that the young aviator had landed in Paris after a flight of only thirty-three and a half hours, Don gave a whoop of joy that could be heard for blocks. He and Uncle Rod danced a war dance and no one — not even the baby — minded in the least.

A few weeks later, Don and his cousin Harry stood in the window of Harry's father's office on Fifth Avenue in New York City. They were watching the great parade that welcomed Colonel Lindbergh on his return from his flight to Paris.

The sidewalks and windows were full of people. The bands played gaily. In the parade were soldiers, some on foot and some on horseback. Many policemen were seeing that everything was done in an orderly manner.

An automobile came by in the parade with the top pushed back. Colonel Lindbergh sat on the pushed-back top. He had been asked to do this so that people could see him better.

He smiled and waved at the cheering people, but he looked a little tired.

"I'll bet he wishes he was in an airplane and away from all the crowd," said Don.

"Oh, I don't know," said Harry; "it must be fun for him to hear all the people cheering. Anyhow, I'm glad we saw him come back."

Don said afterward to Uncle Rod, "I didn't want to say it to Harry, because it sounds like boasting; but I don't think seeing Lindbergh in the parade was half so exciting as seeing him start off, all alone, that morning in the rain."

"I agree," said Uncle Rod; "it'll be a long, long time before we forget that, Don."

— JEAN Y. AYER.

WHICH IS RIGHT?

Write on your paper the numbers from 1 to 10. Choose the right words to finish each sentence and write them on your paper after the number of the sentence.

1. Curtiss Field is a great flying field

    on Long Island.
    in New Hampshire.
    in Minnesota.

2. Raymond Orteig offered a prize to the first person who should fly between

    Boston and London.
    Quebec and Berlin.
    New York and Paris.

3. Nungesser and Coli started from Paris and
   were lost.
   were successful.
   returned to Paris.

4. Charles Lindbergh flew to Curtiss Field
   from St. Louis.
   from California.
   from Nova Scotia.

5. Lindbergh decided to go to Paris
   with one companion.
   with two companions.
   with no companions.

6. Lindbergh had become expert in flying while
   with a circus.
   in the navy.
   carrying mail.

7. He started on May 20, 1927
   at noon.
   in the morning.
   in the evening.

8. At this time, he was
   twenty-four years old.
   twenty-five years old.
   twenty-six years old.

9. He flew from New York to Paris — three thousand miles — in

thirty-three and one half hours.
forty-three and one half hours.
fifty-three and one half hours.

10. Lindbergh came back to New York

at once.
a year later.
several weeks later.

Things to Do

1. You can read about Lindbergh and other fliers in *Aviation Stories*, by Jay Earle Thomson, in *Riders of the Winds*, by Edward Shenton, and in other books. Later you will want to read Lindbergh's own story of his famous flight, *We*.

2. Pretend that you saw Lindbergh start, as Don Wills did, and write a letter telling some one about it.

3. Copy these words and write the meaning after each. Look up in your "Short Dictionary" those you do not know.

ailerons	hangar
aviator	monoplane
cockpit	motor
controls	throttle

PLAYING AIRPLANE

1. How to Make the Airplane

When you go up in an airplane, the pilot will perhaps let you steer the plane, if there are two sets of controls. So you had better practice first. You can learn by playing that you are an aviator.

Here is the way to make a cockpit, or pilot's seat. Make a seat in a big box, or

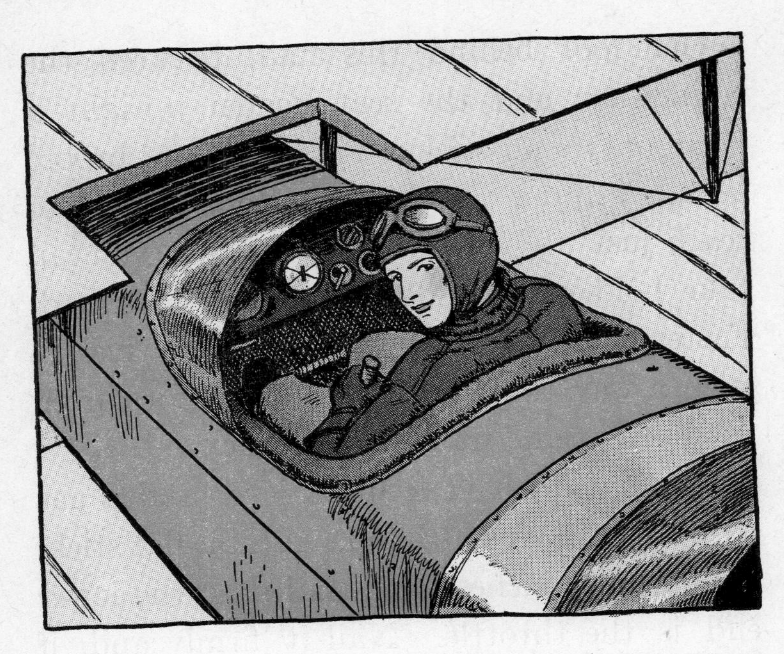

sit in the box in a low, straight armchair with high arms. Looking over the side of the box is like looking over the side of an airplane.

Make a rudder-bar about two feet long, for your feet. Nail it in the center with a long nail going through a small block into a heavy plank. The plank should run lengthways along the middle of the floor of the big box.

One foot behind this nail, between the rudder-bar and the seat, fasten upright a straight, round stick. Part of an old broom handle will do. It should be long enough to reach just above your knees so that you can take hold of it easily when you are seated. Fasten it to the plank with a wire or swivel, in such a way that it can be moved both from left to right and from front to back.

You should have a spark lever and a gas throttle at your left hand. A thin, flat stick, four or five inches long, nailed at the lower end is the throttle. Nail it firmly and, if you can do so, bend the pointed end of the nail over so that it will stay in place as you move the throttle backward and forward. A nail driven halfway in and bent upward will do for the spark control.

Now that your cockpit is all ready you can learn how aviators fly their real planes.

Before we really go for a ride in our airplane, let us find out what makes it fly.

Just think of your kite as it flies. It is the wind that holds it up. The wind is moving air. Even though we can't see it, we can feel it when it blows hard. Sometimes it blows strongly enough to rip big trees from the earth. The wind moves sailboats, turns windmills, and blows clouds across the sky.

If there is no wind blowing, you cannot fly your kite well. But you can get it up a little way by running fast with it. Pulling it quickly through the air is quite the same as having the air blow against it.

The propeller of an airplane pulls the airplane through the air just as if an unseen giant were running with it on the end of a long string.

The propeller is on the front part of the airplane. It is like a big fan, or like the screw that pushes a big ship through the water. It is turned by a motor like the one that turns the wheels of an automobile. Only this motor is much bigger and goes at a high speed. When the two blades of the propeller are turning fast, you cannot see them clearly. They are just a round blur.

Don't ever get near one when it is moving. It would break to bits almost anything it hit. It makes a great wind blow behind. This wind is sometimes strong enough to blow a boy down flat.

If the wind stops, a kite comes down. If the propeller stops, the plane comes down. But the plane does not wabble and flop like the kite coming down, because the pilot steers it.

Gravity, which pulls all falling things to the earth, pulls the airplane down when the propeller stops. Its speed in coming down makes enough wind against its wings to make it float instead of dropping straight. It glides gently like a sled coasting downhill. The airplane levels out when it nears the ground and so does not come down on its nose.

This airplane motor, like an automobile

motor, runs by the use of gasoline. It has spark plugs to explode the gasoline. The force of this explosion pushes the pistons, the pistons turn the crankshaft, and the crankshaft turns the propeller around.

You make the motor go faster by moving the throttle, or gas lever, forward. The force of the explosions inside the motor is greater because more gas flows in when you move the throttle forward.

2. How to Operate Your Plane

To steer your plane left or right, work the rudder-bar with your feet, just as you would steer a bobsled or a coaster.

Be sure to move the stick — the one made from a broom handle — when you move the rudder, and move it in the same direction that you move the rudder.

In turning, you must "bank" the airplane. You know how hard it is to turn a corner when you are running over flat ground.

You can't help skidding beyond the corner. An airplane will skid if you turn with the wings level. If you turn left, the left wing must go down and the right wing go up. To turn right, put the right wing down and let the left wing go up.

You move the wings by putting your stick to the side toward which you are turning. The ailerons, or little movable flaps at the end of each wing, tilt the plane when you move the stick from side to side.

Pulling the stick back or pushing it forward makes the airplane go up or down.

Before really flying, you must learn to move these controls properly. The skillful pilot flies without any more thought of the stick and rudder than you have in keeping your balance on a bicycle. He just does the right thing without thinking how.

Now we will pretend that you have had a good deal of practice and that you are ready for a real flight.

Tell your mother not to worry as you are only going to Labrador, Greenland, and the North Pole, and will be home in time for dinner. See that your men have filled the gas tank. Put on your helmet and goggles. Climb into your seat. Take hold of the controls and look around to see that the rudder and ailerons work properly when you move the stick and the rudder-bar.

This is a land plane that you are flying, so you will take off from the ground. The plane is in front of the hangar. The wind is blowing toward us. The field before us is wide and clear.

Have the people who are looking on stand back from the plane. Before your mechanic approaches, be sure that your spark is turned off. When he takes his place to crank the motor or to spin the propeller, turn the spark lever to "on," and say, "Contact," so that he will know that the motor is ready to fire.

The propeller starts to move around. You advance the throttle to give it more gas. Soon it is humming smoothly. It is making quite a loud roar, and the gas is only partly on, at that.

You "give her the gas," and I — your passenger — hold onto my seat and act as if I weren't a bit afraid. But I really expect you are going to give me a very thrilling ride.

Now we are rolling across the field with the motor roaring as loudly as it can. Dust flies up behind us. Soon we are going so fast that the tail of the plane lifts off the ground. You push the stick forward a little bit to keep the plane from rising too soon. Finally it feels light. There is a firm air pressure against the controls, and you know that the wind is lifting the swift wings. So you pull back on your stick and up we go!

Hurray for the brave pilot!

There is a tall tree right in front. But, quick as a wink, you pull back the stick and

"zoom" over it. But don't forget to push the stick back to center when you have cleared it. We mustn't climb too fast.

There's the church steeple at our right. Rudder-bar and stick swing to the right and over we go to see if there are any pigeons living in the belfry. As we skim over the houses, people look up in surprise. They didn't know you were an aviator.

The birds in the trees are scared and fly up wildly as we pass above them. Perhaps they think some new kind of hawk has come to chase them. You can fly faster than they. But you couldn't catch them because they can turn and dodge more quickly than you can.

In a jiffy we have reached the steeple. Our pilot banks up steeply on one wing tip. Swish, swish, we are pivoting sharply around the tall spire. We spin so fast and so very close to the roof that the people below surely must be gasping.

3. What Happens as We Fly

You mustn't thrill your passenger too much at first. It might scare him. Or he might get sick and not enjoy your tricks. Some people do feel ill on the first flight. It is something like being seasick.

Look at that little white cloud. It seems to be as tame as a lamb and not very far away. Let's chase it and play leapfrog with it.

There, now! It didn't take so long to catch up to it with your motor going full speed. My, can't we climb fast! Not up straight like a baseball when you bat out flies, but at a good, steady angle.

The cloud is now right in front of us. It looks quite solid, doesn't it? I wonder if you dare to drive right into it? You think it might give you a hard bump? Well, try and see. I promise it won't hurt you.

Rur, rurr, rurrr! We are charging at it. Closer, closer. Why, you are gripping the stick as hard as if you expected to crash against it. Here it comes.

Swish! Just as soft as feathers! We didn't feel anything. The cloud is nothing but a pile of fine mist. In some places it is thick and you can't see through it. In other places it is merely a thin, filmy, drifting veil.

In a moment we are out at the other side. Now look back at the cloud. Only a few seconds ago we passed through it and it is already far behind. Think how fast we must be going. There are no marks up here with which to check our speed and most of the time we don't realize that we are going more than a mile a minute. If we were close to the ground and the trees and telegraph posts were whizzing by, it would take our breath away.

Down below, the college athletic field spreads out. Doesn't it look small? The concrete stadium looks like a little teacup. It would take you several minutes to walk across the field but in your plane you shoot over it in less than half a minute.

Here comes another airplane toward us. I think he wants to play with us. But we don't want to play with him. We don't know how well he can fly. So we will not get too close. Bad accidents happen when two planes touch in the air, because of the great speed at which they are going.

But watch how we whiz by this other plane. As each plane is going at the rate of a hundred miles an hour, we approach at the rate of two hundred miles an hour. Like two fast express trains passing in opposite directions — zip, we've come together and gone again. Already the other is far away.

Having shown me how well you can handle the plane in ordinary flying, you open up the throttle and hold the stick back firmly. We climb steadily up, up, up — one thousand, two thousand, three thousand feet, and finally five thousand feet in the air. Almost a mile high! Let's keep on going up to five thousand, two hundred, and eighty feet. There! Now we are just exactly one mile above the ground.

You can tell how high you are by noticing how the hand points on the dial of the altimeter. The altimeter is the little machine used for measuring the height to which an airplane rises.

Isn't the land wonderful as you look down? Everything seems so neat and orderly. It looks like a map. See how the river winds like a silver thread. There's another river in the distance that you never knew was there — and lots of tiny ponds, whole forests of trees, and farms, and railroads. Crisscrossing everywhere are roads. To see the people on them, you have to peer sharply. The automobiles and trucks seem no bigger than bugs, and they seem to move along slowly like bugs.

Did you notice the way your town melts into the country? In the center, houses and tall buildings are close together. Gradually they thin out until you see only farms and woods. To you, living in a town, everything seemed to be streets and houses. The open country seemed a far-away thing. Now your town looks small and the country seems very near to it.

The next time you feel that the world is full of uninteresting houses and streets and that it is too closely built up for you to have any fun, think of how little room the towns really take up. They are just tiny dots in the huge world of trees and grass.

4. Doing Stunts

You came away up here to have plenty of room to do stunts. The way to put the plane back on an even keel after almost all stunts is to nose dive a few hundred feet and then straighten out. Therefore you want to have plenty of room between yourself and the ground. Bad crashes happen when the ground comes up at the plane before the pilot is ready.

Now, we'll loop the loop!

Nose the plane over for a minute in order to increase the speed. Then pull back the stick steadily and firmly — and *hold* it back. Surely such a brave pilot won't become nervous and put the stick forward again when he sees the nose of his plane rising away above his head. Will he? No. He hangs

on and keeps his eyes in front of him — right on the dashboard. If he looked over the side, he would only see the sky, anyway, and would not know where he was.

Over we go!

Upside down, with sky and land all mixed up and churning around together; then right side up once more.

You did it so well that we sat firmly in our seats. Not at all what people expect to do when they are on their heads in the air.

Wasn't it funny when we were coming down? I peeked over the side and the whole world seemed to be rolling over. I thought it was the world doing a somersault, not we. But when the horizon between the sky and land came in sight, I knew we were almost right side up again.

Although it seemed to take a long time to flatten out after that loop, we only lost two hundred feet. We are still more than five thousand feet in the air. That height is safe enough so that we can do some more stunts. We will try stalling.

On leaving the ground, we found that we couldn't climb straight up. We had to go up at an angle. What do you suppose would happen if we pointed the plane up too steeply?

Why, the motor wouldn't be strong enough to hold us up and we'd stop going ahead; and you know what happens when a plane stops going ahead. Just what happens to a kite when the wind stops blowing all of a sudden. We should flop down and dive toward the ground.

Now let's try it and see how it feels. Pull back the stick and hold it firmly, keeping the wings level. Up goes the front end! There isn't enough speed to keep it going on over as it did when we looped, because we didn't dive first to pick up speed. The propeller roars and roars as before, but the wind on the wings is calm.

You move the rudder-bar about, but it doesn't steer the plane at all. That's because we have lost headway. We seem to hang in the air for a moment. I don't like the way it feels with the nose of the plane sticking up in front. Do you?

My seat doesn't feel firm. Surely we can't stay this way for a whole second. Something is certainly going to happen.

There!

Snap, and down goes the nose of the

plane! Over and down we go — diving head-first at the ground. It is like what happens when you go over a big hump on a roller coaster. Whee-eee-ee! How we shoot!

This part of it is lots better than hanging up there waiting for the nose to drop. I had thought for a moment that we were going to slide backward. That also can be done in some planes, if you know how.

Now you'd better pull out of this nose dive before we lose any more height or increase our speed too much. Easy there! Don't pull the stick back too hard. The plane is going awfully fast. A sharp pull would put too much strain on the elevator. Gently, a little at a time. The speed is growing less as the plane flattens out. Now you've got it back to its regular position.

What a good pilot you are!

Why didn't we loop instead of stalling?

Because we weren't going fast enough. Before looping, you dived to get up speed.

This time you are going to show me a tail spin.

You start off with the stick pulled back just as if you were going to stall the plane. But instead of holding it straight and keeping the wings level, you kick the rudder-bar away over to one side and shut off the motor by pulling the throttle back.

Then one wing drops and the plane snaps over to one side.

Oomp!

The tail snaps around in a circle of its own. We are banged up against the side of the plane.

Oomp, again! Once more the tail jerks around.

But we don't simply shoot straight down. It feels as if we were first sideways, then topsy-turvy, then all in a heap. The plane is spinning. The pilot's head is spinning. The whole world is spinning. Oomp! We bump again as the tail swishes around.

The plane is heading downward and making a circular movement as it goes, but the tail spins around in a bigger circle than the nose makes.

Don't look about like that or you won't know where you are. Either look at the instrument board or look straight down at the ground along the side of the plane on which the wing is lower.

Now you can get your bearings. Before another one of those terrible snaps comes, let us get out of this spin. Bring the stick and the rudder back to the centre. Soon you will stop spinning and just be headed toward the ground in a nose dive.

Oomp! We shall lose one thousand feet or maybe two thousand feet before this crazy old plane levels out.

There now, pull your stick back, gently but firmly, and open the throttle. There is nothing like a little coasting to put things right.

But what trouble we'd have had if there hadn't been a lot of room below us.

5. Coming Down

You are very eager now to get back to the ground so that you can tell everyone what a thrilling ride you have had.

We'll glide gently down.

Push the stick forward easily. As the stick goes forward, pushed by your left hand, shut off the throttle with your right hand. With practice you will be able to do the two things together very smoothly.

Isn't it quiet! I hadn't realized how much noise the motor was making until you shut it off. Now we can really talk.

Hear how the wind whistles through the wires of the plane. It sounds very pleasant. If you glide too steeply and too fast, the wires will warn you by screaming.

See! We are right over the landing field again after flying over what seemed like most of the world. If you keep on gliding straight ahead this way, we'll land over at the other side of the town. So you bank the wings and turn around over the landing field several times while we are gliding toward the earth. Then when we are low enough to land, we shall be at the right spot. That is what we call *spiralling down.*

During this glide, the motor is not shut off entirely. The throttle is adjusted so that it does not close tightly when pulled back, but allows enough gasoline to be drawn into the motor to keep the propeller turning over slowly.

As we glide, the propeller turns around quite rapidly. But it is not just the motor that is turning it. The air is also turning it as it brushes past. The way to shut the motor off entirely is to turn the ignition switch to the "Off" position. We haven't spoken of this switch before, but you know, of course, that it is just below the throttle.

Do you notice how warm it is getting? Every foot we coast seems to bring us to warmer air. I can even smell the growing things on the surrounding farms.

The closely buttoned flying suits we are wearing have become rather uncomfortable. When we were a mile in the air, they were just warm enough.

Get ready to land now!

The altimeter says that we are at one thousand feet. But that is wrong. We are much lower than that — about eight hundred feet, I should say. The altimeter lags behind when we drop fast.

After more experience, you will know how high you are from the ground and will be able to plan your landing accordingly.

First, make sure of the direction of the wind. Just as in flying a kite, you must run into the wind when landing and taking off.

See that smoke blowing from the powerhouse chimney. See that flag waving from

its mast and that cloth bag on the roof of the hangar. They all blow in the same direction and show that the wind is the same as when we were taking off. It is blowing across the field toward the hangar, as before.

Therefore we must glide down over the roof of the hangar. Doing this will take us out across the field before we touch ground.

Nearer, nearer comes the land. Hold the plane steady. Don't let it turn or let either wing drop. Now we're about ten feet off the ground. Pull back your stick. Now hold the plane there. Keep it off the ground for a moment until it slows up a bit. See, it's settling down.

Chunk! Wheels and tail touch the ground together. And we roll slowly along to a gentle stop.

Home again!

— John F. McNamara (*Adapted*).

Flying Terms

Here are some words used in connection with aviation and some definitions. Copy the numbers of the words and put after each number the letter of the definition that belongs with that number.

1. aileron
2. bank
3. cockpit
4. controls
5. hangar
6. landing field
7. nose
8. nose dive
9. pilot
10. rudder bar

A. To tip an airplane to one side or the other.

B. A piece of ground large and clear enough so that aircraft can land on it or take off from it.

C. The front of an airplane where the propeller is located.

D. The open spaces in an airplane where the pilot and the passengers sit.

E. The parts of an airplane by means of which the pilot guides it.

F. A person who operates an airplane.

G. A building where aircraft are housed.

H. A movable part of the wing of an airplane.

I. The foot bar by means of which the rudder is moved.

J. A movement of an airplane straight downward with the propeller first.

Things to Do

1. The story you have just read is taken from a book by John F. McNamara called *Playing Airplane.* You will enjoy reading it. It is easy to read and explains quite clearly what a flyer does. *Zoom* by George R. White is good also, but it is harder to read than the other. If you are interested in the different kinds of flying machines that have been made since flying began you will want to see *The Picture Book of Flying* by Frank Dobias.

2. It would be interesting to get a large box and make a make-believe airplane like the one described in *Playing Airplane.* Then you could practice some very safe flying.

CHAIROPLANE CHANT

If everyone had a flying machine
The size of a small armchair,
Then day after day, in the promptest way,
I'd go out to take the air.

I'd shift a lever and press a brake,
And buzz out into the blue.
Oho, the bushels of air I'd take,
Flying to call on you!

As I skirted a steeple and skimmed a roof,
With engine whirring loud,
I'd meet you coming for dear life, humming
Around the rim of a cloud.
We'd dodge a swallow and duck a crow,
And you would cry, "Whoopee,
I was going to call on you, you know —
Were you coming to call on me?"

It's rather awkward to chat, of course,
From a high-geared chairoplane,
So we'd buzz away. But the very next day
We'd meet in a sky-blue lane,
With wind in our wings, and the way all clear,
And I'd sing, "Ho, halloo,
Were you coming to call on me? O *dear*,
I was going to call on you!"

— NANCY BYRD TURNER.

THE TIMID TRUCK

Once there was a great blue motor truck. When he went through the town blowing his horn, all the people ran out of his way as fast as they could go.

"Honk, honk, honk!" cried the motor truck.

The hens fluttered back and forth across the road.

"Honk, honk, honk!" cried the motor truck.

The dogs ran out and barked.

"Honk, honk, honk!" cried the motor truck, and the children shouted as the big blue truck went booming by.

But away down inside his engine the truck was not big and brave at all. He was really very timid! When his driver drove fast, he was so afraid that he could scarcely see out of his headlights. But his driver paid no attention to him. He was quite a reckless driver. He delighted in passing other cars on the road and in making what he called " record runs."

" Record runs," moaned the motor truck, " they'll be the death of me! If I were going to make a record, I'd rather make one for taking more time than anyone else, not for going faster. I can't see why everybody is in such a hurry. They say, ' Safety First.' Well, my driver always tries to be first and forgets about the safety. ' Safe and last,' that's going to be my motto! "

But the driver thought his truck was much too cautious, and all he did was to put on more gas. Away they rushed, up hill, down hill, across bridges, through the woods, and away across the country.

One day a small car passed the truck.

" This will never do," said the driver and he pressed his foot on the gas.

"It will do very nicely, if you will just use sense," sighed the truck. "I like to have things pass me. I'd let everything on the road pass me if it wanted to!"

The driver only pressed the harder on the accelerator, and they flew after the little car.

"Honk! Honk!" tooted the truck's horn. "*Get out of the way!*"

The truck did wish that his horn had been taught to say, "If you please." It sounded so much better.

The little car ahead stayed right in the middle of the road. The driver of the truck grew angry.

"*Honk! Honk!*" tooted the horn again.

"Road hog!" muttered the driver.

But the little car ahead stayed right in the middle of the road. Not one inch to the right did the little car go.

"That car is only using common sense," said the truck. "This is no place to pass."

The driver swung his truck over to the left side of the road. He honked yet once again. He was determined to pass the little car.

"Careful, careful," begged the truck. "Watch out. There's mud at the side of the road."

But his driver only put on more gas. Suddenly the truck had a strange, sinking feeling. Something was giving way beneath him!

"My wheels!" he screamed.

Round and round spun the wheels, but they could not get a grip on the soft mud.

Round and round they spun, but not one inch forward could they go. The truck felt himself sinking. He stood still for a moment and then he began to tip.

"Whatever will become of me?" moaned the truck.

His driver jumped to the ground. It was an easy matter for him! He didn't weigh two tons and a half!

The truck felt himself tip further and further. Then, — bump, — bang, — and over he fell into a daisy field. The grass tickled his engine. A bunch of flowers was caught in his bumper. He was in a sorry plight.

"Oh, my gears and crank-shaft! My engine is in a hundred pieces!" groaned the truck, while tears of gasoline ran down his hood.

The little car had stopped. "I am so sorry," he said. "Didn't you see the mud? I didn't dare give you any more room."

"It was all my driver's fault," answered

the truck. "I told him not to pass you and he would not listen. I will never let him drive me again. I hope they take his license away. I suppose he'll just leave me here to rust. He doesn't care what happens to me!"

But the driver *did care.* As he looked at his great truck lying there helpless, he began to feel ashamed of himself. He agreed with the truck that he had been stupid.

The little car carried him to the next town. Back he came as soon as he could with four strong horses and several men. They fastened iron chains to the truck.

"You'll never get me up," he said, "not if you bring forty horses."

"Ho, ho," laughed the horses. "Who used to do all the pulling before you trucks were invented?"

The driver ran around doing all he could to help the truck.

"Poor old fellow!" the truck heard him mutter.

At last the chains were in place. The horses pulled and the chains tightened. A jerk — and the truck was on his wheels. Again the horses strained. The truck began to move forward. Bump — and he was back on the road again!

"There you are!" cried the driver with delight.

"My trouble is not over as easily as that," grumbled the truck, "not with all these strange feelings in my engine."

They tried to start the engine but it would not start, so the horses were fastened to the truck again and into the town they pulled him. He squeaked and complained at every turn of the wheel.

For five days they worked on him at the garage. They took him all to pieces and they put him all together again. His driver never left his side. He stood by to see that the work was well done and he ordered the best of everything. He spared no pains or money.

The truck began to feel quite differently about his driver. He had made a muddle of things, but now he was certainly doing his best to make it up.

At last the garage men were through. They gave the truck a new coat of blue paint that made him look bigger and bluer than ever. When that was dry, he was ready to start out into the world again.

"I've learned my lesson," said the driver to the garage men as he paid his bill. "I'm going to drive carefully from now on!"

The truck listened, but for some strange, new reason he did not care whether his driver was careful or not — he who had always been so timid! Something unexpected had happened inside the great blue motor truck. *He was no longer afraid!*

"When you have lived through an experience like that, you find it does not pay to be afraid," he said to the other cars in the garage. "Think of what happened to me, and here I am as good as new."

When they started out, he took the first corner on two wheels. The driver nearly jumped off his seat with terror. They passed every car on the road. Nothing that the driver could say did any good.

"I can't seem to manage this truck since the accident," he complained. "I must have lost my nerve."

The truck chased hens just for the fun of it. He backfired so hard at a policeman that he was nearly arrested for carrying concealed weapons. Then he tried to run round and round a " Keep to the right " sign that stood in the middle of the road, blinking one stupid red eye at them. He was trying to see how close he could go without knocking the silly thing down. At last he went too close and the thing toppled over and blinked its red eye for the last time.

" I can't stand this any longer," cried the driver, " I'm going to give up trucking!"

This made the truck stop to think. Did he really want to lose his driver? They had been through much together! There was no telling what kind of new one he might get. He considered matters carefully. There is always a middle way in this life. Perhaps it would be better to be a little more careful.

So he settled down to a sober gait, and, from that day to this, there has not been a more reliable truck or a more reliable driver in the entire service.

— CAROLINE D. EMERSON (*Adapted*).

Improve the Order

These sentences are not in the right order. Read them over carefully and decide what the right order should be. Write on a paper the numbers of the sentences to show in what order you would arrange them. The first number you should put down is 4, for sentence 4 should come first.

1. The driver of the truck was quite reckless.
2. One day a small car passed the truck.
3. He delighted in passing other cars on the road.
4. Once there was a great blue motor truck.
5. The little car ahead stayed right in the middle of the road.
6. When he had been repaired, the truck became reckless.
7. They flew after the little car.
8. It took five days to repair the truck.
9. He fell over into a daisy field.
10. The truck did not want to lose his good driver.
11. Suddenly the truck had a strange sinking feeling.
12. So the driver and the truck both became more careful.
13. The driver said he would give up trucking.

14. He chased hens, backfired at a policeman, and knocked over a "Keep to the Right" sign.

15. Four horses were brought to move the truck back into the road.

Safety First

Suppose you were living on a street along which the big blue truck sometimes passed. Give five safety-first rules that you would need to remember.

Things to Do

1. The story "The Timid Truck" is taken from *A Merry-Go-Round of Modern Tales*, by Caroline D. Emerson. Perhaps you will like to read some of the other stories in this book.

2. Here are three columns of words. Each column is to be arranged in alphabetic order. When the first letters of words are alike, we arrange them by the second letters. In the first column, *band* should come first and *beat* second.

bird	crowd	funny
band	camel	forever
branch	cedar	factory
boxes	children	fiddle
bushes	clean	flower
black	cooking	feather
beat	curl	free

A SHORT DICTIONARY

1. Helps in Pronouncing

The Short Dictionary gives the more difficult words that are used in *Magic Hours*. It tells the meaning of each word, as it is used in *Magic Hours*, and shows how the word should be pronounced. You can tell from this list of guide words how to pronounce the vowels according to the marks that are over them:

ā as in lāte	ĕ as in mĕt	o͞o as in fo͞od
ă as in hăt	ẽ as in hẽr	o͝o as in fo͝ot
â as in câre	ī as in kīnd	oi as in oil
ȧ as in ȧsk	ĭ as in hĭll	ou as in our
ä as in fär	ō as in ōld	ū as in ūse
ē as in hē	ŏ as in nŏt	ŭ as in ŭp
	ô as in fôrk	

The accented syllable in a word, that is, the syllable that is spoken most strongly, has this accent mark (′). For example, the first syllable is the accented one in this word, *ac′ci dent.*

You will find the guide words at the foot of each page, so you will not need to turn back to this page when you are finding out how to pronounce a word. The word at the left top of each page, on pages 398–408, is the first word defined on that page. The word at the right top is the last word defined on the page.

2. Dictionary Word List

A

ac cel′er a tor (ăk-sĕl′ẽr-ā-tẽr), a device for increasing speed. In an automobile it is the lever by which the amount of gasoline supplied to the engine is regulated.

ac′ci dent (ăk′sĭ-dent), an unexpected happening.

ac com′plish (ă-kŏm′plĭsh), to complete; to bring to a successful finish.

ad vice′ (ăd-vīs′), an opinion offered for some one to follow; counsel.

af fec′tion ate (ă-fĕc′shŭn-āt), loving; having warm regard.

a hoy′ (ȧ-hoi′), a word used in hailing a ship to attract attention. It is like "hello."

ai′le ron (āl′ē-rŏn), a movable part of the wing of an airplane.

air′-brake (âr′-brāk), a brake operated by compressed air.

A lad′din (ȧ-lăd′ĭn), a young man who appears in a story in a book called *The Arabian Nights*. He had a magic lamp, by means of which he could get anything he wanted.

an noyed′ (ă-noid′), irritated; teased; made angry.

anx′iety (ăng-zī′ē-tĭ), worry about something that may happen.

anx′ious (ănk′shŭs), worried about something that may happen; uneasy in mind because of some possible misfortune.

ap peal′ (ă-pēl′), to call on some one for help or sympathy.

as ton′ish ment (ăs-tŏn′ĭsh-mĕnt), great surprise; amazement.

au′di ence (ô′dĭ-ĕns), a group of listeners.

a vi a′tion (ā-vĭ-ā′shŭn), the art or science of flying.

a′vi a tor (ā′vĭ-ā-tẽr), a person who operates aircraft.

B

bag′gage (băg′āj), the trunks, bags, etc., that people take with them when they travel.

ban dan′na (băn-dăn′ȧ), a large handkerchief, usually red or blue, with white or yellow figures on it.

Bar′ba ry (bär′bȧ-rĭ), a region in North Africa.

---

lāte, hăt, câre, ȧsk, fär, hē, mĕt, hẽr, kīnd, hĭll, ōld, nŏt, fo͞od, fo͝ot, fôrk, oil, our, ūse, ŭp

bay′ber ries (bā′bĕr-ĭs), small hard berries — the fruit of the bayberry bush.

be ret′ (bā-rā′), a small round cap, much used in France.

bish′op (bĭsh′ŭp), a clergyman of importance in various Christian churches.

black′smith (blăck′smĭth), a man who works in iron with a forge — one who shoes horses, donkeys, and mules.

boom′ing (bōōm′ing), giving a hollow roar—such a noise as is made by waves or cannon.

bum′per (bŭm′pẽr), the metal bar at the front of an automobile that serves to deaden the shock of a collision.

but′ler (bŭt′lẽr), the head manservant in a house where there are many servants.

C

Ca na′ry Is′lands (kȧ-nā′rĭ ī′lănds), a group of islands in the Atlantic Ocean, northwest of Africa.

car bol′ic ac′id (kär-bŏl′ĭk ăs′ĭd), a poison taken from coal tar. Weakened by mixing with water or other liquid, it is used to kill germs.

car na′tions (kăr-nā′shŭns), flowers with a sweet, spicy perfume. They belong to the family of pinks.

cat′er pil lar (căt′ẽr-pĭl-ẽr), the wormlike larva of a butterfly or moth.

caus′tic (kôs′tĭk), burning; able to eat away by chemical action.

cav a lier′ (kăv-ă-lēr′), a horseman. The word is only used, however, if the horseman is a gay, elegant, aristocratic person.

char′coal (chär′kōl), charred wood, used in place of coal.

chinked (chĭnkt), filled with something to keep out cold air; as *The cracks in the wall were chinked.*

chris′tening (krĭs′nĭng), baptism.

cin′der (sĭn′dẽr), a partly burned coal; ash.

clear′ing (klēr′ĭng), a piece of land cleared of wood.

cleft (klĕft), a crack; an opening; a space made by splitting.

Cle o pa′tra (klē-o-pā′trȧ), a queen of Egypt about two thousand years ago.

cock′pit (kŏk′pĭt), the open spaces in an airplane in which the pilot and passengers are seated.

Co li′ (cō-lē′), a French aviator who was lost while trying to fly from Paris to New York.

col′lie (kŏl′ĭ), a Scotch shepherd dog.

com bine′ (kŏm-bīn′), to unite or join.

com mit′tee (kŏ-mĭt′ē), a group of persons appointed to take care of some matter.

com mo′tion (kŏ-mō′shŭn), disturbance; excited motion.

com′pass (kŭm′pȧs), an instrument used for finding directions. It has a needle or pointer that always points north.

com plain′ing (cŏm-plān′ĭng), grumbling; finding fault.

Con nect′i cut (kŏ-nĕt′ĭ-cŭt), a state of the United States of America.

con′science (kŏn′shĕns), a person's own knowledge of whether his conduct is good or bad.

con trols′ (kŏn-trōls′), the parts of an airplane by which the pilot operates it.

cop′per as (kŏp′ẽr-ăs), a green substance used in making ink and black dyes.

cos′tumes (kŏs′tūms), the clothing worn by people representing characters in a play; dresses.

court′iers (kôrt′yẽrs), people in attendance at the court of a king or other ruler — not servants, but people of standing.

crank′shaft (krănk′shȧft), part of an automobile.

crocodile (krŏk′ō-dīl), a large, thick-skinned, long-tailed reptile that lives in and near water in tropical countries.

cross′beam (krŏs′bēm), a supporting beam that lies across another beam.

cuck′oo (ko͝ok′o͞o), a European bird. A cuckoo clock has a small wooden cuckoo that pops out on the hour, with the sound of a cuckoo, to tell the time.

curt′sey (kûrt′sĭ), a kind of bow made by women as a matter of politeness. It consists of sinking the body and bending the knees. No longer used except by very young girls.

cyl′in der (sĭl′ĭn-dẽr), the piston chamber of an engine.

D

dam′age (dăm′āj), injury, harm.

dash′er (dăsh′ẽr), the part of a churn that moves up and down and keeps the cream moving.

de scen′dant (dē-sĕn′dănt), one who descends from others; as, children, grandchildren, etc.

de spair′ (dē-spâr′), hopelessness.

de tached′ (dē-tăcht′), separated; disconnected.

dike (dīk), a bank of earth used to keep water back; a dam.

dis ap pear′ance (dĭs-ăp-pēr′-ăns), passing from sight; vanishing.

dis gust′ (dĭs-gŭst′), feeling caused by something very unpleasant; dislike.

dis tress′ (dĭs-trĕss′), suffering; misery; unhappiness.

dis′trict (dĭs′trĭkt), a definite portion of a town or city.

dis turbed′ (dĭs-tûrbd′), confused in mind; upset.

doi′lies (doi′lĭz), small napkins, or ornamental pieces of linen or lace for a table.

dol′drums (dŏl′drŭmz), dullness, sadness.

drag′on (drăg′ŭn), a make-believe animal that appears in stories — always very fierce and dangerous.

draw′bridge (drô′brĭj), a bridge which can be lowered to let people across or raised to keep them from crossing.

drub′bing (drŭb′ĭng), a beating; a thrashing.

duf′fer (dŭf′ẽr), a stupid person.

E

earth′en ware (ûrth′ĕn-wâr), dishes made of baked clay.

E dam′ (ā-däm′), a town in Holland, famous for its cheeses.

em broid′ered (ĕm-broid′ẽrd), decorated with needlework.

e merged (ē-mûrjd′), came out.

em′pha sis (ĕm′fȧ-sĭs), in speaking, stress or force of utterance given to certain words or syllables.

en cy clo pe′dia (ĕn-sī-klō-pē′dĭ-ȧ), a book or set of books giving information about many subjects.

en dure′ (ĕn-dūre′), to bear, to remain firm.

en er get′ic (ĕn-ẽr-jĕt′ĭk), active; full of energy.

e nor′mous (ē-nôr′mŭs), of great size or amount.

en′try (ĕn′trĭ), a hall or other place through which people enter.

er′mine (ûr′mĭn), a beautiful white fur obtained from a kind of weasel called the ermine.

e rup′tion (ē-rŭp′shŭn), a breaking out or bursting forth, as from a volcano.

ex pen′sive (ĕx-pĕn′sĭv), costly.

ex plor′ing (ĕx-plōr′ĭng); to search through or range over for discovery.

F

Fi′ji Is′lands (fē′jē ī′lănds), a group of islands in the South Pacific Ocean.

Fonck (fônk), a French aviator who was killed in an airplane accident while preparing to fly from New York to Paris.

foot′man (fo͝ot′măn), a man-servant who attends the door, carriage, table, etc.

foun′tain (foun′tĭn), a spring of water; a structure from which water flows.

fu′ri ous (fū′rĭ-ŭs), full of fury; very angry.

G

gait (gāt), manner of walking.

ga rage′ (gȧ-räzh′), a place for housing automobiles.

gauge (gāj), a device for showing the height of water in a boiler.

Gauls (gôls), people who, in the time of the ancient Romans, lived in France and northern Italy.

ge ra′ni um (jē-rā′nĭ-ŭm), a plant with deeply cut leaves, bright flowers, and a pleasant odor.

gil′ly flower (jĭl′ĭ-flou-ẽr), a kind of pink with a spicy scent.

gleam′ing (glēm′ĭng), shining.

gob′lin (gŏb′lĭn), a make-believe creature — a kind of sprite usually thought of as ugly and mischievous.

grack′le (grăk′l), a rather large, glossy black bird with purple tints on head, tail, and wings. It likes to live in orchards and destroys many harmful insects. It sometimes eats the eggs of other birds.

grav′i ty (grăv′ĭ-tĭ), the force that attracts bodies toward the center of the earth.

groove (gro͞ov), a channel; a furrow; a rut.

gur′gling (gûr′glĭng), flowing in a broken noisy current, as water from a bottle.

H

hang′ar (hăng′ẽr), a building where aircraft is stored.

hay′cock (hā′kŏk), a pile of hay.

heaved (hēvd), forced; lifted up.

hedge′row (hĕj′rō), a fence made of small growing trees or shrubs.

Hein′rich Schul′ze (hīn′rĭk sho͝olt′sĕ), a man in "A Molasses-Cake Story."

high′way (hī′wā), a main road.

I

ig ni′tion (ĭg-nĭ′shŭn), act of being set fire to or lighted.

im pressed′ (ĭm-prĕst′), deeply interested; affected.

in ves′ti gated (ĭn-vĕs′tĭ-gāt-ĕd), looked over carefully; examined into.

J

jaun′dice (jôn′dĭs), an illness that causes the skin to look yellow.

Jer′i cho (jĕr′ĭ-kō), a city in Palestine; also the name of the stuffed parrot in "The Cat and Susannah."

K

knight (nīt), in old times a man of special military rank — a soldier — who served some great nobleman.

L

Lab′ra dor (lăb′rȧ-dôr), a peninsula in the northwestern part of North America.

La van′da (lȧ-vän′dȧ), the name of the goat in "Little Tonino."

le′ver (lē′vẽr), a bar of metal, wood, or other rigid substance, used to exert pressure at one point of its length by the application of a force at a second point, and turning at a third point on some fixed support.

li′lac (lī′lăk), a shrub with fragrant flowers.

lime (līm), a substance obtained from limestone or shells.

lo ca′tion (lō-kā′shŭn), place of settlement.

lye (lī), a strong caustic solution, often made by running water through wood ashes.

M

maj′es ty (măj′ĕs-tĭ), grandeur. The word is used in speaking to or about a king or queen, as "Your Majesty," "His Majesty," "Her Majesty."

Mar′i gold (măr′ĭ-gōld), a flower. The word is sometimes used as a girl's name.

mar′vel ous (mär′vĕl-ŭs), wonderful; very surprising.

Mi′das (mī′dȧs), the Greek king in the story "The Golden Touch."

Min ou′ (mĭn-ōō′), the name of Tonino's cat in the story "Little Tonino."

mis′chie vous (mĭs′chĭ-vŭs), full of mischief; naughty.

mi′tre (mī′tẽr), a kind of tall decorated hat — the official headdress of a bishop.

moat (mōt), a deep, wide, water-filled trench around a walled town or around a castle. A drawbridge was let down over the moat when people wished to enter or leave.

mo las′ses (mō-lăs′ĕz), a dark, thick sirup drained from sugar when that is being made.

mon′o plane (mŏn′ō-plān), an airplane that has only one main supporting surface.

mo′tor (mō′tẽr), something that causes regular motion — as a steam, gasoline, or electric engine.

Mount Ve su′vi us (mount vē-sū′vĭ-ŭs), a volcano in Italy, east of the bay of Naples.

mu′ci lage (mū′sĭ-lāj), a solution of gum, used to make things stick together.

musk′rat (mŭsk′răt), a large water rat, found in North America. It has a long tail, webbed hind feet, and dark brown fur.

mus′ter (mŭs′tẽr), to gather; to collect; to assemble.

mys′tery (mĭs′tẽr-ĭ), something unknown and puzzling; something that cannot be explained.

N

non′sense (nŏn′sĕns), matters of no importance; folly; silliness.

Nor′way (nŏr′wā), a country on the northwestern part of Europe.

Nun ges ser′ (nūn-zhĕ-sā′), a French aviator who was lost while trying to fly from Paris to New York.

O

ob′e lisk (ŏb′ē-lĭsk), a four-sided pillar, tapering as it rises and ending in a pyramid.

or′chard (ôr′chẽrd), an enclosed piece of land in which fruit trees grow.

or′deal (ôr′dēl), a severe trial; a trying experience.

Or teig′ (ôr-tēg′), a Frenchman living in America, who gave the Orteig Prize, which Lindbergh won by making the first flight from New York to Paris.

P

pad′dle (păd′ėl), a wooden instrument with a broad blade used for pressing the buttermilk out of butter.

page (pāj), in old times, a boy who was being trained to be a knight.

pan′ther (păn′thẽr), a large fierce animal belonging to the leopard family; a cougar.

pa′tience (pā′shĕns), power of waiting calmly for something.

pell-mell′ (pĕl-mĕl′), in great haste and in no particular order.

per spi ra′tion (pûr-spĭ-rā′-shŭn), sweat.

per suade′ (pẽr-swād′), to win over some one to believe or do something.

Piet (pēt), a character in the story "Sinterklaas and Pieterbaas."

Pie′ter baas (pē′tẽr-bäz), a character in the story "Sinterklaas and Pieterbaas."

pi′rate (pī′rāt), a sea robber.

pis'tol (pĭs'tŭl), a short firearm for use with one hand.

pis'ton (pĭs'tŭn), a sliding piece of metal, moved by, or moving against, fluid pressure — usually a short cylinder moving in a cylinder.

piv'ot ing (pĭv'ŭt-ĭng), turning on a fixed point.

pix'ie (pĭk'sĭ), a pixie (or pixy) is a fairy.

Plin'y (plĭn'ĭ), a Roman naturalist and writer.

Plym'outh (plĭm'ŭth), a town in eastern Massachusetts — the oldest town in New England.

Pom pe'ii (pŏm-pā'yē), an ancient city, near Naples in Italy, that was buried by an eruption of Mount Vesuvius.

por'cu pine (pôr'kū-pīn), a rat-like animal that has sharp spines mingled with its hair. It uses the spines as a means of defense.

pos'tern (pōs'tẽrn), a back door or gate. In the old days, the postern door or gate was often used as a way of escape.

pot'ash (pŏt'ăsh), a white salt, made from wood ashes and used in making soap, glass, and other things.

pot'ter y (pŏt'tẽr-ĭ), dishes made from earthen materials. The name is also given to the building where such dishes are made.

prac'ticed (prăk'tĭsed), done over and over again.

pre'cious (prĕsh'ŭs), very valuable; greatly loved.

preened (prēnd), trimmed or dressed with the beak. The word is used chiefly of birds.

prime (prīm), early life; youth.

prog'ress (prŏg'rĕs), moving forward; advancement.

pro longed' (prō-lôngd'), made longer.

pro posed' (prō-pōzd'), suggested; offered a plan.

pro test' (prō-tĕst'), to object to something; to speak against something that has been suggested.

pro vok'ing (prō-vōk'ĭng), irritating; vexing; annoying.

R

rac coon' (ră-ko͞on'), a North American fur-bearing animal, chiefly gray, with a bushy ringed rail.

ra vine′ (rȧ-vēn′), a deep trench made by running water.

re li′a ble (rē-lī′ȧ-b'l), fit to be relied on; trustworthy.

re verse′ (rē-vûrs′), turned back; backward moving.

rheu′ma tism (ro͞o′mȧ-tiz'm), a painful disease that attacks most often the joints or muscles.

ri dic′u lous (rĭ-dĭk′ŭ-lŭs), laughable; not worthy of serious consideration.

rogue (rōg), one who is mischievous or frolicsome; also, a rascal or cheat.

ro mance′ (rō-măns′), an interesting story.

roost (ro͞ost), to sit or sleep on a perch; to perch.

royal (roi′ăl), suitable for a king or queen.

S

sau′sage (sô′sāj), meat chopped fine and highly seasoned and usually enclosed in a skin of some kind.

scan′dal ized (skăn′dăl-īzd), horrified; shocked.

scen′er y (sēn′ẽr-ĭ), the painted scenes or hangings, and other equipment, of a stage on which a play is given; the general appearance of a landscape.

scent (sĕnt), odor, smell, fragrance, perfume.

sen′ti nel (sĕn′tĭ-nĕl), one who watches or guards.

sex′ton (sĕks′tŭn), an official of a church who takes care of the building, rings the bell, attends to burials, etc. In old times, he also arranged for baptisms and did other duties.

shark (shärk), a large fish with sharp teeth — dangerous to man.

shift′ed (shĭft′ĕd), moved; exchanged; changed.

shiv′ered (shĭv′ẽrd), shook, trembled.

shriek′ing (shrēk′ĭng), screaming; crying out in a high, piercing voice.

sim′ple ton (sĭm′p'l-tŭn), a foolish or silly person.

Sin′ter klaas (sĭn′tẽr-kläz), the name Dutch children call Saint Nicholas.

slight′ly (slīt′ly), to a small extent; somewhat.

snort′ing (snôrt′ĭng), puffing out air noisily.

sol′emn ly (sŏl′ĕm-ly), very seriously.

so lu′tion (sō-lū′shŭn), the act or process by which a substance is absorbed into a liquid substance. The liquid that results is also called a *solution*.

solved (sŏlvd), cleared up; explained.

soot (so͝ot), the fine, black powder, chiefly carbon, that colors smoke and that settles on objects that the smoke passes.

spi′ral ling (spī′răl-lĭng), winding around.

spit (spĭt), a slender, pointed, metal rod used to hold roasting meat in a fireplace.

stadium (stā′dĭ-ŭm), a place where athletic contests are held, with tiers of seats for people looking on.

stall′ing (stôl′ĭng), in the case of an airplane, this means losing, for any reason, the air speed necessary for support or control.

star′ling (stär′lĭng), a bird about $8\frac{1}{2}$ inches long with dark feathers, yellow bill, and red legs. It likes to live near buildings and walls.

stock (stôk), a kind of low, thick-growing gillyflower, found especially in countries near the Mediterranean Sea.

stub′born (stŭb′ẽrn), obstinate; unreasonably unwilling to give in to another's opinion.

stunt (stŭnt), a feat or performance that is striking because of the skill or strength it shows.

sug ges′tion (sŭg-jĕs′chŭn), hint; indirect request.

Su san′nah (so͞o-zăn′ȧ), a character in the story "The Cat and Susannah."

T

tal′low (tăl′ō), the suet or fat of sheep or cattle.

tap (tăp), a hole or pipe in a cask or barrel through which liquor is drawn.

ter′race (tĕr′ās), a hillside arranged in a series of levels one above the other, like stairs.

ter′ri to ry (tĕr′ĭ-tō-rĭ), a large stretch of land. In the United States, a section that had not yet been made a state was called a territory.

teth'ered (tĕth'ẽrd), fastened by a rope or chain of some length.

throt'tle (thrôt''l), a valve for regulating the supply of steam, gas, or air to an engine.

tre men'dous ly (trē-mĕn'-dŭs-ly), very greatly; to a wonderful extent.

trice (trīs), a very short time.

trout (trout), a handsome fish belonging to the salmon family. There are several different kinds.

tun'nel (tŭn'ĕl), an underground passageway.

tu reen' (tŭ-rēn'), a large dish for holding soup.

turn'ta ble (tŭrn'tā-bl), a revolving platform for turning a locomotive about.

V

vat (văt), a large tub or cistern used in dyeing, mixing liquids in large quantities, etc.

ve ran'da (vē-răn'dȧ), a piazza, an open portico usually with a roof.

vine'yard (vĭn'yȧrd), an enclosure or plantation where grapevines are grown.

vit'ri ol (vĭt'rĭ-ŭl), a sulphate (or salt) derived from copper, iron, zinc, etc., used in making ink and in dyes.

Viv'i en (vĭv'ĭ-ĕn), the name of a prince in the play "The Golden Goose."

vol ca'no (vŏl-kā'nō), a hill or mountain from which steam and melted rock come forth.

W

weath'er-vane (wĕth'ẽr-vān), a contrivance fastened to some high place, as the roof of a building, that turns with the winds and shows the way the wind blows.

wis ta'ri a (wĭs-tā'rĭ-ȧ), a climbing shrub with purple flowers.

wood'chuck (wo͝od'chŭk), a burrowing, fur-coated animal, found in the United States and Canada.

MAGIC